The River Arrow at

£2·25

The Little Gosling

THE fluffy gosling flapped his wings
    And splashed out from the tiny
pond,
He waddled through the bulrushes
    And off towards the farm beyond.

Across the field with daisies and
    Red pimpernels he made his way,
While swallows dived so fast above
    A chugging tractor cutting hay.

A herd of brown cows stood to watch
    Him s-q-u-e-e-z-e beneath the farm-
        yard gate,
The sheepdog didn't notice as
    He ate the dinner from his plate!

He stopped to look inside a barn
    And saw the farm cat fast asleep!
Behind him, bright-eyed mice played
        games
    Or climbed the straw blades, high and
        steep!

The little gosling joined the hens
    That scratched the ground for favourite
        grain,
Exploring till the sun went down
    And time to waddle home again!

* *

— *Eileen Sweeney.*

* *

4

People's Friend Annual

•

CONTENTS

BACK COVER Loch Tummel

THE CURE FOR ALEC'S ILLS

A LEC SANDERSON opened the door of the solid fuel stove and threw in two blocks of dried turf. A puff of peaty smoke billowed out into the small kitchen as he slammed the steel door shut.

"The one thing I must not do," he said aloud to the empty room, "is to get involved with her."

He had found that when a man lives alone even for a few weeks, it becomes normal to talk aloud sometimes, even though there is no-one to hear. And it was nearly four weeks now since he had rented this cottage on the edge of Clonarty village in the deep South-West of Ireland.

by S. W.
RAEBURN

He went to the kitchen window and looked out towards the white stucco farmhouse, the domain of Mrs Kathleen Mulligan. Mrs Mulligan was a problem, and he had come all this way from London just to get away from problems. The strain of the past two years had sapped almost all his stamina. The fabric of life had crumbled, and now he was here in this sleepy, dreaming valley, to rest and try to pick up the pieces.

Two years ago he had felt a lucky man — a happy marriage, a flourishing electronics business and no cloud on the horizon. Then it had all begun to happen — slowly. At first there had been no hint that his wife's weakening muscles concealed a rare form of multiple sclerosis. But as the months passed, it became clear that nothing would arrest its relentless progress.

And the fates, as it happened, were doubly cruel. The long, intensive nursing went hand in hand with a sharp down-turn in the business. Alec Sanderson's efforts to save it included taking risks and borrowing heavily. But his care for Margaret came first and foremost, and when her death occurred just a year ago, he knew he had also sacrificed all hope of saving the firm he had once spared nothing to build up.

He hadn't realised then how near his own health was to a breakdown until his doctor and life-long friend spelled it out for him — a total slow-down for some months and a lifestyle immune from emotional anxieties. So here he was, with his business wound up, with staggering debts still to be repaid, and a tiny residue at the bank allowing him possibly a few weeks' respite to rest and sort out the future.

W HEN he had contacted the Irish Tourist Board and rented the cottage unseen from an equally unseen Mrs Mulligan, his mind's eye had imagined her as a white-haired, apple-cheeked matron with baking flour up to her elbows, a warm, lilting brogue and a motherly smile. More vaguely, he also pictured an elderly husband who kept a dairy herd and played the fiddle.

The real Mrs Mulligan was revealed as a twenty-six-year-old widow with high cheek-bones and dark lustrous eyes, which, as the Irish say, the fairies had put in with dirty fingers. She was tall, and her neck, for some silly reason, reminded him of what an ivory pillar should look like.

As he paid her the first month's rent in advance he had noticed that only her hands belied this almost goddess-like impression. They were red and scratched, and marked by what was undoubtedly hard manual toil. As she handed him his receipt, her smile wasn't exactly motherly, but the memory of it remained with him after he was settled in the cottage.

Otherwise, she was crisp and businesslike with hardly a trace of brogue. "Since my husband died, I've run this place as a market garden," she told him. "I can sell you almost any type of vegetable you name. Also I have a couple of cows and there's fresh milk every day. If I'm not around, Liam my handyman will help you. He's quite ancient and a bit slow, but he can handle casual sales."

Alec was impressed. He was relieved, too, that the real Mrs Mulligan was not the chatty, mothering old soul of his imagination, who, with kindness, might ferret out his circumstances and pity him. All he wanted was solitude, peace and time to think. When he felt ready, he had skills to offer the world. There were opportunities somewhere, some day, far from sad memories.

These four weeks had passed smoothly, exactly as he had planned — shopping in the village, long walks over the bright green countryside between fuchsia hedges, and glasses of dark foam-topped beer in pubs that never seemed to close. Occasionally he went further afield. His executive-style car had long since been sold and replaced with a rusting old Mini. Evenings, under the soft light of a paraffin lamp, he wrote copious notes and lists relating to a business he might painfully rebuild one day with the aid of a bank loan and new energy.

The one disturbing factor was that he could not stop thinking about Mrs Mulligan. He was at a loss to understand it, or when it had started. Almost unawares, he had been going too often down the narrow stony path that led to the farmhouse. The evidence stared him in the face — the vegetable rack in the larder was loaded with lettuces, tomatoes, courgettes and peppers that he did not need.

Lately, when he found himself standing by the window hoping for a glimpse of the slim figure with her midnight dark hair swinging at her shoulders, he would curse himself for a madman and drive off crazily until he found himself halfway to Killarney.

LOVE, infatuation, call it what you like — but this was the last thing that should be happening to him. The uncertainty, the pining, the anxiety, the whole catastrophe . . . And to make it worse he was just a passer-by without a penny to his name. Well, the cure was obvious — stay away from now on. Tomorrow he must go and pay next month's rent. After that, well, he would arrange with old Liam to deliver the milk and any other needs.

Only, Liam would probably talk about her. Kathleen was her name, for Liam, a compulsive talker, had told him so. "She's some woman that," the old man had confided with his thumbs in the armholes of a tattered waistcoat. "Up with the dawn she is, summer and winter, and work, work, like a beast on a treadmill. She had a hard enough life with Mulligan with his cantankerous ways. And it's no easier now, no life for a lone woman, but she needs to keep the land alive until she sells the place. A brave woman and all. She has brains, too, that one."

Well, Alec reckoned, his call next morning would be his last for some time if he was to carry out his resolve.

Nevertheless, when the time came he shaved and dressed carefully, choosing his best shirt from the bag that contained all his wardrobe. Kathleen Mulligan saw him coming and called him cheerfully into the kitchen. She was weighing cucumbers for packing and marketing, but she brushed it all aside in favour of morning coffee.

Fixed upon him were the violet eyes that had been haunting him on wakeful nights. "I was beginning to think you had left us. But Liam tells me you've been getting around the country."

Alec ignored the opening that could have led him to lower his guard.

With an effort he resisted the temptation to confide in her, to exchange reclusion and caution for the warmth of an easy relationship.

"I like it here, Mrs Mulligan," he said. "There couldn't be a better place for a rest and time to think."

She handed him a mug of coffee, and her nearness brought him the awareness of a faint perfume. "Yes, it's the right place if one wants to be alone for a bit. By the way, my name's Kathleen. What's yours?"

"It's Alec, or sometimes Sandy, which fits both Alexander and Sanderson." He looked at the stacked boxes, each labelled for its destination. "How long have you been doing this? Liam tells me you work too hard."

Her slow smile, as usual, etched another souvenir for his memories. "Hard work is always relative. Depends how much you like what you're doing."

"And you like it?"

"Only for a time. They say working close to the soil has a healing effect. But soon I must move on. I used to teach at a school in Cork. Meanwhile I try to preserve this place as a going concern."

"And making a fine job of it all on your own."

He saw the flush of pleasure at his words. "There's Liam, of course," she said. "He comes for a while every day. Looks after the cows and helps a little with the picking. I'm afraid I can't afford any more than that."

Alec put down the coffee mug and got to his feet, handing her the cheque. "I mustn't hold you up then. And if it all gets too much, I'd be glad to help."

The smile this time held a touch of sadness. "You'd better not. I might come to depend on you."

ALL the way back up the path her last words stayed in his mind. *I might come to depend on you.* There it was — the need was there, both in her and in himself. It would be easy to cement a friendship. But mere friendship would be intolerable, and as for anything more, he was bad news. The help and support she needed was of a kind that wasn't his to give.

For all the following week he found things to do, places to go and people in bars to talk to. He felt a stab of guilt when Liam brought the milk instead of fetching it himself. He would stay until the end of the month. Then it was goodbye, Mrs Mulligan.

It was on the second Monday of the month when it seemed that leprechauns had taken up the case of Alec Sanderson. Liam trudged up to the cottage door, clanking the milk can on the step and fingering the grey stubble on his chin. "Mother of God, and it's the bad news I'm bringing this morning. Mistress Mulligan has hurt herself and cannot stir from the house."

As with all shocks, the full meaning did not register at once with Alec. "Hurt herself?" he repeated stupidly.

"She fell and twisted her foot, real bad. The doctor has been and bound it up but she must not stand on it for a while. Sure, and it's the queer way we are in down at the farm now that this has happened."

Suddenly, the crisis cleared Alec's head as nothing had done for weeks. To weigh his actions now against his own problems would be out of the question. He gulped down the coffee and toast that served for breakfast and made his way to the farmhouse.

She was lying on a couch with her bandaged foot propped on a cushion. Under the tan her face showed the pallor of pain, and his heart went out to her.

"It's not as bad as it looks," she said with an attempt at a laugh. "I can get around with a stick, and there's nothing broken."

"From now on," Alec said with an authority he had not felt for a long time, "you get around just as little as possible while I take over. I'm no farmer and not much of a gardener, but I can pick vegetables and drive them to market and sell them. All I need is to be told what to do."

She shook her head. "It's sweet of you, Alec, but a few days won't make much difference. Probably just a few over-ripe tomatoes, Liam will do his best."

"From what I hear," said Alec grimly, "it will be a bit more than a few days. And Liam's best is a long way below my worst. And he can't drive a car."

"You can make some coffee if you like," she said, and the look in her eyes made him feel a little taller.

He took the remark as a flag of surrender, and within ten minutes he was worming from her all the information he needed. Tomorrow a consignment was due in Cork, and all the picking and packing must be done today.

It was late September, and the harvesting of aubergines, peppers, beans and tomatoes was at its height. The winter crop of leeks had to be hoed, and another thousand leek seedlings transplanted. The long polythene-covered tunnels also contained melons which in the mild climate could be ripened without artificial heat. But ventilation and humidity had to be controlled.

Deep In The Countryside

FERN-LINED lanes,
　　Warm and still.
Brim-full
Of quiet air,
Which gently parts
To let the idling traveller pass.
And stirring
Makes soft breathings in the grass.
Then closing back.
Traps there within
The evocative scents
Of growing green,
And pollen dust
From bright-faced buttercups.

— D. E. Hawcutt.

Alec drove Liam to unprecedented efforts, and when the day was over, with the produce packed and loaded in the van, he felt physically drained but happier within himself than he had been for months.

He hurried back to the farmhouse, his thoughts on the task of cooking a meal, but Kathleen was already leaning on a stick, preparing food. He knew better than to bully her when she had to move, but he made sure of being two steps ahead of the work until dinner was served and cleared.

It would have been churlish to leave immediately, and as the evening wore on he succumbed to her gentle probing about his life. Inevitably, although as sketchily as possible, he told her the story.

"At the moment I'm little more than a vagrant," he concluded. "I'm going to get back in business, but it's a long haul. A single-handed battle — just like yours."

Her eyes held his in a steady gaze. "There's a limit to how long one can do that. It's a lonely road."

He sat in silence, then stood up to go. "I'll be over first thing in the morning."

She made a helpless gesture. "I shouldn't let you do this."

He paused at the doorway and grinned. "You haven't any choice. Just try to stop me."

IT was like that for five days. But the news of the mishap spread among the local dairy farms, and by the time Friday came, a flock of helpers were dropping in and doing a short stint in the house or in the field.

Kathleen's injury healed faster than he had reckoned, and once she was out and about and fit to drive the car, he felt the time had come to melt into the background again. He finally resorted to calling each day or every second day.

He avoided addressing her by her given name, even though she used his with a frequency that showed a strong liking for him. It was not that he imagined this through some male vanity — one sensed these things and knew them for truth.

The waves of rapport that passed between them were almost tangible. Yet one part of him repeated the warning that he was an encumbrance she was better without. The past week had shown him that she had friends and good neighbours, people who cared.

In the solitude of the cottage, where even small things like the very kitchen utensils and the crockery seemed to contain her personality, he fought to use cold reason against the subtlety of love. In his view, it was impossible to stay. And once gone, whatever had started to grow between them would wither and eventually die.

It was on a day when the weather turned wild that he made up his mind. A tearing gale roared through hedges and fields, bending the trees and bringing the death warrant of summer.

Alec spent some hours cleaning the small kitchen and tidying the cottage to the point where all signs of occupation had gone. He raked out the stove and scoured the saucepans until they shone. His personal packing was simple, and all that he had brought with him went into a single bag.

It was after dusk when he had finished. He would drive away very

The Cure For Alec's Ills

early in the morning and head for the docks at Rosslare. Meanwhile, the real ordeal lay ahead. If he was leaving, then better to go quickly. Now was the time to walk down to the farmhouse, put a cheeful face on it and say goodbye.

In the darkness, gusts of wind funneled down the stony path so that it was hard to keep his feet. At times the glow of her downstairs windows was the only guide to keep him out of the overgrown ditch.

By ordinary standards it was a late call. She looked startled as she answered his knock on the door. Then her pleasure at seeing him was plain. "I've just finished making blackberry jam. So now you can join me in a drink. You can try my elderflower wine."

THE warmth and aroma in the farm kitchen wrapped round him like a cloak, and that, with the vitality of her presence, almost dizzied his senses. The contrast to the now austere emptiness of the cottage filled him with unease. It would be difficult to make this a casual goodbye.

He waited until she had put a wine glass in his hand, and for moments he sat watching her deft movements as she replenished the open fire with birchwood logs.

"Perhaps it's a bit late to be dropping in, but I've been putting the cottage in order."

She laughed. "Was it in such bad order?"

"No, but I wanted to leave it as clean as I found it. And it's time I was moving on."

She was brought up short, poised, with a log held halfway towards the blaze. It seemed to Alec quite a time until she stopped gazing into the fire and turned to look at him.

"You don't mean . . . now?"

He gulped down half the contents of the glass. "I'm afraid so. It's best that I go tomorrow."

She stood up from the fire and wiped her hands on her gay, striped apron. "But I thought . . . well, it's only the middle of the month. I mean, it's all a bit sudden."

Inwardly Alec cursed himself for a clumsy fool. It had seemed the easiest way — to spare himself, and perhaps her, too, the strain of a lengthy impending departure during which his determination might have failed. And now she was feeling shut out, denied any right to his plans or thoughts.

"It's not that I want to leave here," he said desperately and with genuine conviction. "But I have to get to London and make a start somewhere. And if I don't go now —" He stumbled over the words. "If I stay any longer I won't be able to leave."

They remained looking at each other, and to Alec it felt as if the dark blue eyes were probing deep into his mind. "You'll be back?" she asked at length.

It took all his willpower not to make the easy, impossible promise. "I don't know," he said tensely. "It will depend on how things go."

The west window rattled against the assault of the gale, and she

13

moved over to tighten the catch. "I see." Her voice was small and hurt. "We must settle up then. I owe you about half a month's rent."

Humiliation brought drops of sweat to Alec's forehead. "For God's sake, there's no need for that. Nothing was further from my mind."

She was at once contrite. "I'm sorry, Alec. I had no right to bring that up just now, or to ask you any questions. I hope everything goes right for you. I don't know how I would have managed without you."

He stood up and the nearness of her was like a charge of electricity. He knew that if he even touched her hand he would be lost. He found himself saying, "If I can start a new business and pay all my debts, I may come back — if by then you're still here."

She smiled, one of her sad smiles. "There are so many 'ifs' for both of us. It's the 'now' in life that always seems difficult." Then, with a brisker tone, "You'll start off in the morning?"

"Yes. Probably quite early."

He was at the door now, and as he made to open it the frame shuddered and protested under the storm.

"You must take a torch.You'll never see your way up the boreen."

"The boreen?"

"The Irish name for it. What we call the little road to the house."

"I'll remember that," he said, "and a lot of other things. But I don't really need a torch. I know every yard of the way."

He opened the door and the blast of wind tore at her dress and sent dark strands of hair across her eyes.

"Take care, and goodbye!"

"Goodbye, Mrs Mulligan! Goodbye!" The words were snatched from his lips and whirled away for ever on the wind, perhaps unheard.

The stony path was bordered on both sides by grassy banks, and above that by dense hedges of bramble and fuchsia. It was pitch black, but at times the scudding clouds were rent apart and a full hunter's moon lit the tossing trees.

It was more by instinct than by these fitful gleams that Alec found his way up the winding road. Once he glimpsed the wooden shed where cattle fodder was stored and he knew he was almost halfway back to the cottage. The old timbers of the shed groaned, and the corrugated iron sheets on the roof hammered under the madness of the storm.

Ayrshire Morning

A BREATH of air disturbs the leaves
Rustling against the window pane.
The birds' first chorus of the dawn
Rises, falls, then comes again.

Window watching, I see the mist
Roll up the valley like a flood,
Over the backs of the feeding herd
Standing mute in the meadow mud.

Now the sun's first warming beams
Set the clouds with golden edges,
Mellow the brooding line of moor,
Colouring the granite ledges.

Daybreak opens to my eyes
As Adam once saw Paradise.

— *Edgar W. Goodall.*

Suddenly, with a noise like thunder, the shed flew apart and fragments of wood sailed over his head, crashing off into the night.

It was less than a minute later when he looked back over his shoulder and saw a pin-point of light, wavering uncertainly and coming towards him. For a moment the wind died and there was no sound except faint footsteps on the road behind.

THE torch-light grew brighter and nearer now, until a break in the clouds revealed the figure of Kathleen. She stopped by his side and he could hear her hard breathing and vaguely see her face, white against the collar of a dark coat.

"You're all right, then?" she said breathlessly.

"Of course. But I'm afraid your shed's gone with the wind."

In the thin, unearthly light of the moon she looked scared and defenceless. "I don't care about that. I thought . . . I was sure something must have happened to you."

A sudden savage gust caught them and she staggered against him. He found himself holding her, shielding her from the force of the gale, and it seemed that his arms had no power to let her go.

They stood there in the teeth of the elements until clouds raced overhead and snuffed out the moon. He could feel the warmth of her breath, and strands of her hair being lashed against his face. There was only the wind and themselves and the darkness left in the world.

"I don't want you to go," she murmured.

He kissed her then because it was inevitable. With all his power of will he wrenched his mind back to reality. "I have to go. Even if you came with me, all I have to offer is toil and trouble."

She moved from his arms but gripped him by both shoulders. "I'm used to that. Because you're that kind of man, you think you have to do it all on your own. But there are two of us, and I'm not fragile. We need each other. You knew that, didn't you?"

"A long time ago."

"Well, don't stand there. Come in from the cold."

"I ought to go back to the cottage!" he shouted against the gale.

"What a silly idea!" she shouted back. "You see, I know you, Alec. I'm sure you've drawn the fire, polished the stove, and the place is probably like a tomb. What's wrong with a log fire and a hot drink? And surely we've got plenty to talk about."

It was strange, Alec thought to himself a little later, being back again after saying goodbye, sitting here in the deep armchair, watching her swift, beautiful movements, her eyes sparkling and her black hair all awry like a gipsy's. It was like a dream, a dream that had come true which he couldn't fight any more.

"If that shed hadn't blown away," Alec said, "I would probably never have seen you again."

She turned from the drink she was pouring and the smile was radiant with mischief and love. "Don't you believe it. I would have been up before dawn. Something else would have happened — like somebody letting the air out of your tyres." □

HONEYMOON SURPRISE

by
KATHLEEN
KINMOND

IT had been a lovely wedding in the setting of an old English village with a picturesque church dating back to the sixteenth century.

Sandra had looked as beautiful as Ian Watson had known she would, and it had made his day to see his parents looking at her just as lovingly as they looked at their only son.

"And so you're off now," Ian's father, Albert, said to the bride and 'groom as they prepared to leave on their honeymoon. "I don't suppose there's any point in asking where you're going?"

The young couple looked at each other and smiled.

"Just motoring around, actually," Ian said. "We might head for Devon and Cornwall, but we haven't thought beyond that."

"I'm sure everyone has enjoyed themselves," Nan Watson said to her new daughter-in-law. "Your parents have been wonderful hosts."

Sandra blushed slightly.

"I'm glad to hear that. They were only sorry it was just that bit too far for the older members of your family to come all the way from Scotland."

Ian's father nodded.

"Yes, I know the two grannies in particular were disappointed, but it would've been too much for them."

As Ian and his bride moved in to speak to some of the other guests, Sandra spoke softly.

"Why don't we head for Scotland on our honeymoon instead and see all the folk who couldn't come so far because of age and one thing and another?"

Ian looked at her in surprise.

"On our honeymoon?" he exclaimed. "There'll be plenty of time to visit the family later. I don't want to share you with anyone else just yet."

"Just think what it would mean to the two grandmothers," Sandra persisted. "And the other people I've heard about. Meg in the wheelchair, for instance."

A S they stood talking to two of her aunts, Ian considered Sandra's suggestion. Perhaps there was something in what his young wife had said. What a super way to start their married life together, by giving other people some pleasure.

When they next found themselves alone Ian told Sandra he'd changed his mind.

"We could spend a leisurely week in Devon and Cornwall and then go north to visit relatives during our second week," he suggested. "Shall we phone them now and let them know?"

They rang Gran Watson first, for the simple reason she had always been his favourite grandparent and he her favourite grandson.

She sounded delighted and near to tears to think they'd taken the trouble of telephoning her, and thrilled to bits when they said they'd be up to see her.

They next rang Gran Davidson, who sounded just as delighted at the thought of seeing them both and said she'd make a special clootie dumpling for their visit.

"Whatever did she say? What's a clootie dumpling?" The English bride giggled as they came off the telephone.

"Something like a Christmas pudding," Ian told her. "Clootie being the Scots word for cloth. You'll love it. Now, let's tell Mum and Dad about our suggested visit."

"Yes, they'll probably be pleased to hear we're meaning to come north," Sandra agreed.

"Oh, that's a wonderful idea," Nan Watson said enthusiastically. "You'll spend a night with us, of course. I'll get the spare room ready for Saturday. I don't suppose you've any idea of when you'll arrive?"

"Well, I think we'll probably take about two days from the south coast — save us breaking our necks completely. We'll try to arrive on Saturday afternoon," her son said, "then we can visit folk in the evening."

"We'll look forward to that," Nan said as she kissed them both goodbye. "Have a wonderful week together."

Everybody went outside to see them off and refused to let Ian remove the various "just married" notices decorating the car.

T HEY had an idyllic week in Devon and Cornwall, with the sun shining every day. They marvelled at the red sandstone rocks at Dawlish, enjoyed motoring in the narrow Cornish lanes, and were genuinely surprised when other hotel guests teased them as honeymooners, not realising the aura of happiness they shed everywhere they went.

They left on the Thursday to give themselves plenty of time for the journey north.

Sandra had already met his two grandmothers, but as they drove along he told her of others he'd like to take her to meet if they had time.

There was one person they simply had to make time to visit, Ian told her, and even as he said it, Sandra knew who he was meaning.

She'd heard about Meg before. Her husband ran a bakery and as a schoolboy Ian had gone round with Meg delivering bags of rolls. Then later, when Ian was learning to drive, Meg would go to the doors while he practised on the van. But recently she'd suffered a stroke.

O N Saturday, they stopped for a light lunch at a roadside café, and before they left Ian glanced at his watch. They'd probably arrive at his parents' home round about four, he estimated, which would give them time for a quick snack before visiting the grandmothers.

A few miles from their destination they stopped to tidy their hair. Sandra applied fresh make-up.

"Is that all right?" she asked her young husband before they drove on again and he simply had to take her into his arms and tell her how lovely she looked and how much he loved her.

As they arrived at his parents' home they were surprised to see so many cars outside.

As soon as they drew up, first one then another face came to the window, and next moment the front door opened and to their astonishment, people seemed to pour down the pathway to meet them.

His mother arrived at the car door first and said in breathless explanation to her son that they were just a few relations and friends they'd invited to meet them.

"But the two grans?" Ian wanted to know as he helped Sandra from the car. "We were to be visiting them this evening."

"Yes, we knew that and invited them to come here instead. They arrived about an hour ago as excited as children. Here they are, look!"

They were just as Nan said and both hugged and kissed the young couple and led them indoors where they could see a table laid in the dining-room, simply groaning with a selection of cold meats, salads, exotic-looking sweets and bottles of wine.

B EFORE they were all invited to sit down, Albert saw to it that all the guests had their glasses charged with wine and proposed a toast to Ian and Sandra.

"It's just like another wedding reception for those who missed the real one," Sandra whispered happily in Ian's ear as his father invited everyone to sit down at the loaded table.

"There's only one important person missing," Ian said quietly to his wife.

"Yes, I know," she answered, "Meg."

His mother, sitting one away from him, had sharp enough ears to hear the remark.

"Meg was invited," she said quietly. "But since her stroke she's been in a wheelchair and she can't get about very easily. Her husband is away on business today and we haven't heard whether she'll be able to get here or not. But," she added with a chuckle, "I'm almost sure she'll be having a jolly good try to come."

The grandmothers had been placed on either side of Ian and Sandra and were eager to hold their attention and give them all their news rather than hear the young couple's.

"I baked a cake for the party," Sarah Watson was confiding in her grandson, "and we're going to have it later in the evening with a cup of tea."

"But when did you know all this was going to happen? We had no idea there'd be a party."

The two old ladies giggled like young girls.

"Well, as soon as Nan and Albert got home they told us they'd thought of having a surprise party for you," one of them said.

"Yes," put in the other old lady. "We all got together and we've been working like hatters all week, I can tell you."

Ian, listening fondly to the two ladies chattering happily, gave his wife's hand an affectionate squeeze under the table.

A FTER the meal, everyone went into the large sitting-room, where, to Sandra's surprise, almost all the furniture had been removed, leaving quite a considerable space.

Don Strachan, one of Ian's school friends, seated himself at the only large piece of furniture left in the room, the piano, and invited Ian to lead off the dancing with his young wife, followed by Albert and Nan, until the room was packed with couples bumping into each other and laughing merrily.

The two grandmothers didn't have partners, but Ian and his father took them up to the next dance, much to their delight. Suddenly a shout from across the crowded room took everyone's attention.

"Look, there's an ambulance outside."

"Meg!" exclaimed Nan delightedly. "She's managed to come!"

She was about to go out to meet her when a thought occurred to her and she stood back.

"I think this is your job, Ian," she told him.

He nodded and smiled and went quickly from the house, almost beating the ambulance driver to the back of the vehicle.

"Hello, Ian," Meg said happily. "Here I am at last, thanks to Louise here." She indicated a pretty young nurse standing beside her.

The ambulance driver quickly manoeuvred a ramp to lower Meg's chair from the vehicle, and when she was safely on the ground she and Ian greeted each other with a hug and a kiss, and those near enough could see there were tears in their eyes.

Just before the ambulance drove away, the nurse placed a large, flat package on Meg's knee.

"You almost forgot your parcel," she said.

"So I did!" exclaimed Meg cheerfully. "And it's all my own work, too."

She carried it carefully on her knee as Ian wheeled her into the house, where Sandra was waiting.

"This must be your wife?" Meg exclaimed in delight. "And just as I expected you to be, my dear, a sweet English girl."

Sandra bent to kiss her on the cheek as Meg handed over the parcel.

"A long and happy married life together," she said. "I made these trays at the physiotherapy and thought you might like to have them."

"Thank you very much," Sandra said warmly, unwrapping the parcel.

It was some little time until the company settled down to dancing again and although Sandra accepted invitations to dance, Ian sat beside Meg's wheel-chair, talking about days gone by and her illness.

"I spend a lot of time in hospital," she told him. "Gordon couldn't cope permanently with me at home." She smiled with no trace of bitterness. "Wasn't it just like the thing that he had to be away today? However, Louise offered to come with me in her off-duty time, bless her, so here I am."

Throughout the evening, Ian and Sandra made sure they spoke to everyone at the party, and Ian introduced her to the relatives she hadn't met before and also his school friends.

"I think your bride's lovely," Don Strachan told Ian warmly, "I just wish I'd seen her before you did! She's a smasher!"

Ian grinned at what was a typical "Don" remark.

"You'll just have to follow my example and find someone like her," he replied.

A S the two boys caught up on news about their careers, Sandra went over to her mother-in-law.

"This has been a wonderful party," she told her. "We thought we were coming up just to call in on the two grannies and Meg, but . . . well, we'll never forget it. Whatever gave you the idea?"

Nan coloured with pleasure.

"Well, on the way home Dad and I thought we might be able to

Country Craft

A FOXY old thing, the village,
 Absorbing all that's new;
Taking up the urban spillage,
 Giving it rural hue.

The lovely green softens the cars
 That sprawl along its bank,
And in the plain pub's poshed-up bars
 Old warmth outweighs the swank.

The little shop's self-service now
 But still sells this and that;
The brisk new bobby's learning how
 To solve it with a chat.

Those glossy homes, old barns they were,
 Are weathering into place;
And young folk, trendy now, still wear
 The honest country face.
 — *Frances Dover.*

21

organise something and of course the idea caught on and everyone had a great time preparing for it."

Shortly afterwards Meg wheeled herself over to Nan and suggested it might be time to ring the hospital for her to be collected.

Don Strachan was near enough to hear what she said.

"Will that pretty little nurse be coming for you again?" he asked.

"Yes, she will," Meg answered. "You know, I wouldn't have been able to come if she hadn't volunteered to escort me on her off-duty."

"Well, well," Don said, smiling broadly, "I must see the two of you off."

When everyone had eventually departed for home, Albert, Nan, Ian and Sandra flopped down in the dining-room, tired but happy.

"It was simply marvellous, Mum," Ian said. "What a wonderful surprise, when all we were expecting to do was to visit the folk who'd been left out of the actual wedding."

Nan smiled broadly.

"Sandra has already thanked us, but — well, as you could see, it gave everyone here a great thrill. I've no doubt it'll be a talking point for a long time. I expect you'll want to be off on your own again tomorrow morning, now that you've seen everyone," she added understandingly.

Ian and Sandra looked at each other and smiled.

And so, next morning, Nan gave them a substantial late breakfast, "to see them a long distance on the road," as she put it.

Ian felt a little sad saying goodbye to his parents again. But as the young couple drove off, Sandra sighed happily as she clicked on her seat-belt.

"Well, that was just super. What a great idea of your parents."

"Well, I like that," Ian exclaimed. "Are you forgetting it was originally *your* idea that we should break our honeymoon to see everyone here, darling? I even needed some persuasion to agree. Remember?"

She smiled and snuggled as close to him as her seat-belt would allow.

He kissed his finger and laid it on her brow as he drove.

"I'm beginning to think what a clever man I am to have made such a smashing choice of a wife," he murmured. □

Tabby-Tom

TABBY-TOM is not unique,
  You'll find a score like him,
Any day of any week,
  Around the city's rim.
He has no class, no pedigree,
  And in a judge's eyes,
A cat as commonplace as he
  Should never win a prize.
And yet, his deep and rumbling purr,
  His dreamy, golden gaze,
His lovely, shining, brindled fur
  Inspired this song of praise.

Abandoned several years ago,
  A scared and starving stray,
Tabby-Tom limped to and fro,
  Until he chanced our way.
We took him in . . . I can't forget
  The sadness and the strain,
Until the broken hip was set,
  And Tom came home again.

The little, scrawny kitten grew
  So quickly, after that,
And very soon he turned into
  A most delightful cat.
Like pussy-willow are his paws,
  His coat gleams silver-grey,
We never see a sign of claws,
  For ever sheathed are they.
Who cares about his ancestry?
  Our Tommy's set apart;
I'm sure no cat could ever be
  Closer to my heart.

Kathleen O'Farrell

M ARIE had been teaching at the forestry school for two weeks when young Tommy Sutherland first appeared. He was just nine years of age, but something about his eyes and manner made him seem old for his years.

"Sorry, Miss. I appear to be thirteen and three-quarter minutes late this morning." He confirmed this aberration by a quick glance at a silver watch hanging from a chain, both of which he quickly returned to his jacket pocket.

On arriving, the boy had divested himself of the duffel coat and the fur-lined, ridged-soled boots which most of the forestry children favoured. Now he wore trainers removed from his satchel.

by AILIE SCULLION

A LESSON FOR THE TEACHER

Snow had come early to this high country and the ground could prove treacherous underfoot, if one were not careful.

Marie had been allotted a schoolhouse attached to the stone building where she taught the children of a scattered community. She felt rather relieved that she did not have to tramp through thick snow each morning in order to reach work. She just had to open the communicating door which separated school from house and she was in her classroom without even getting her feet wet.

A log fire, lit earlier by the handyman, burned at one end of the large room and filled every corner with warmth. Books lined the walls of the classroom and in the storeroom were boxes of all sorts of interesting apparatus which would help to illustrate lessons during the forthcoming months. In here, thought Marie happily, she had everything she required to do her job satisfactorily.

"Where have you been since start of term, Tommy?" she'd asked the boy.

She had noted from her thick register how the boy had been absent those same two weeks the previous year, and how Miss Marjory Wimple, Marie's predecessor, had seen fit to scratch a cryptic remark against the entry.

Impossible child; more impossible father.

"I went fishing with my dad," the boy answered her truthfully. "We've got this cabin up in the mountains."

Tommy had trotted out the excuse without a sign of remorse and indeed there had been a certain amount of pride in the statement. Marie experienced her first moment of disquiet. It was not so much because of Tommy, but rather the father who would have agreed to such neglect of his son's education. In Marie's opinion it was in those two first weeks of a new teacher's term that affinity was created with pupils.

M ARIE CORBY considered herself a dedicated teacher. She had accepted this testing post, not just because a romance had gone sour, but because she indeed saw it as a challenge.

It was one of the most northerly posts in the country, she'd been told, which had gone vacant six times in the past ten years. Such lack of continuity did not augur well for children's education and that was why she had signed a contract for five years, even although she'd been assured there was precious little social life in the area.

Who needed a social life, she'd told herself firmly, when one had three crates of books to read and a television set which could keep her in touch with the rest of the world?

During Tommy Sutherland's first morning at school, Marie decided to carry out an observation test. She began by holding up a series of pictures of trees and calling out the names printed underneath. Later when she repeated the exercise the children should remember the names.

"Oak tree," she called clearly and the children repeated after her. "Oak tree." All, that was, except Tommy.

"That's a sycamore, Miss."

Marie felt humiliated, especially when after glancing at the card she discovered that she'd picked up the wrong one.

B Y Thursday that week, Tommy had been late three times. Each morning he would draw out the silver watch from the pocket of his duffel coat, study its mother-of-pearl face and declare that he was three and three-quarter minutes late, or two and a quarter, or whatever the case might be.

Marie was not usually given to shortness, but it was the boy's air of complacency which annoyed her and so she confiscated the silver watch. Alarm flooded into the boy's dark brown eyes.

"You can have it returned at home-time," she told him.

"Thank you, Miss."

He was greatly relieved. "You see, it belonged to my grandfather. Dad said I could have it so I'd arrive in time in the morning. The wimp . . . I mean Miss Wimple was always on at me about time-keeping."

"Well it doesn't seem to work, does it, laddie," Marie reminded him coldly, and the boy gazed up at her.

"Oh, I wouldn't say that, Miss. It's really accurate. Dad says it hasn't lost a second in thirty years. He's tested it."

On Friday she had to tell Tommy that she would not have him bringing disgusting creatures into class. That was after he had smuggled in a slimy green toad inside his pocket.

He explained how he had found the toad exposed at the bottom of the winter oak where a fox had dug him out from his hidey hole beneath the roots. Tommy went on to say he had disturbed the fox and felt it safer to kidnap the toad until old foxy got tired of hanging around.

When she told him to take the toad outside, Tommy looked shocked.

"Oh, I can't do that, Miss. I'll have to put him back exactly where I found him, else he'll lose confidence. They're creatures of habit."

Marie was not prepared to argue with the boy. Her pride still stung from the sycamore reprimand.

"When does your father get home, Tommy Sutherland?" she asked now, after he'd refused to remove the slimy green creature for the second time.

"He stops at four," the boy answered, "him being the boss like. Dad gets home first, you see, and has tea ready for us both. You could call in and see him any time after that, Miss."

There was something unnerving about a boy who did not frighten easily. Usually the mention of a home visit brought immediate repentance. Tommy simply slipped the offensive toad back into his pocket and walked back to his seat.

At exactly four o'clock Marie set off along the forest trail reckoning it would take her thirty minutes to reach the log cabins where most of the forestry workers lived.

It came to her as she walked that it was turning into a rather pleasant experience. The forest seemed a magical place after the snowfall. Everything about her was touched by white. From tree branches hung candlelike icicles. Spanning trees, huge spiderwebs glistened, now transformed into lace.

There was a flutter of black against the sky and two black crows landed directly above her, sending down a cascade of white dust that clung to her nose and eyelashes and turned her brown hair grey. She suddenly remembered something Tommy had written in the essay she'd set the class to write. The spelling had been atrocious but the content interesting. He'd described black crows flying from the trees, scattering him with diamonds of snow.

Once, she imagined she heard someone call her name softly but it turned out just to be the wind rustling amongst the trees. She gave a quick shiver.

IT came to her suddenly, that it would be quite dark when she had to return home. Oh well, she would just have to ask Tommy's dad to escort her home. After all, it was because of his son's misdemeanours she'd had to come out in the first place.

The path she walked now ran alongside a stream which had also iced over, but occasionally Marie would notice a movement of water breaking between the frozen boulders and it was as she paused to examine this phenomenon more closely that she noticed the small thickset figure beside the tree and let out a scream.

It was just Tommy Sutherland, she realised at once, out of uniform now and wearing a cut-down sheepskin coat with a matching helmet. For some reason she felt like giggling. The boy resembled a miniature Davy Crockett from the legendary wild frontier.

"It's the warm spring underneath," Tommy explained carefully as Marie looked at him dumbly. "It causes the ice to melt in the stream,"

▶ *over*

GREAT BRITON

JOHN BUCHAN

John Buchan, 1st Baron Tweedsmuir, was born in Perth in 1875. Famous for his adventure novels, the best known of which is The Thirty-Nine Steps, Buchan was also a noted statesman — in 1935 he was made Governor-General of Canada.

Perth Bridge

he added knowledgeably, with all the confidence of his youth.

Marie didn't doubt it for a moment. She was beginning to trust young Tommy's knowledge of the forest.

"I thought I'd better come part of the way to meet you," he was saying now, just in case you took a wrong turning. Dad says townies get lost if you turn them three times."

She felt certain the boy did not mean to sound patronising. He was merely carrying out his father's instructions. Marie frowned as she thought about the man she was about to meet.

"Then your father knows that I'm calling?" she asked pointedly. Tommy's face lit up.

"Of course, Miss. I told him straightaway. He's keeping something warm in the oven for you."

It was quite absurd. Here she was intent upon calling a parent to heel regarding his son's shortcomings and the man was "keeping something warm in the oven for her."

"Stop!" The boy's command came low yet urgently and Marie stopped in her tracks, one scarlet leather boot poised in mid-air.

"Look, Miss." Tommy was pointing towards the stream. Marie hadn't noticed the animals approach. An enormous red deer and his mate had come noiselessly away from the forest. The male was clawing at the ice-covered water with small hooves. The large animal also seemed aware of the warm spring underneath for soon the pair were drinking deeply.

Little Raindrops

WELCOME little raindrops
    Coming down in showers,
Bringing sweet refreshment
    To this earth of ours.

Welcome little raindrops
    Falling from the sky,
Watering thirsty flowers
    Lest they faint and die.

Welcome little raindrops
    To fields of growing corn,
And meadows, too, that are
    Refreshed by you at morn.

Welcome little raindrops
    Say apple blossoms, too,
Apples sweet and rose
    We will owe to you.

Welcome little raindrops
    Falling from the sky,
Coming down like jewels
    From your fountain high.

Welcome little raindrops
    Coming down so fast,
Everything looks better
    When your shower's past.

— *Sister Mary Brigid.*

She had never in her life witnessed a scene like this and stood transfixed, the boy by her side, until the majestic creatures drank their fill, wheeled around and leaped off gracefully between snow laden trees.

They must have been standing perfectly still for at least ten minutes and it came to Marie with a clarity that almost hurt . . . this surely was the reason Tommy arrived late for school. Who could avoid pausing to capture a moment such as this, or perhaps even to rescue a toad from the hungry jaws of a fox?

Minutes would stop ticking in Tommy's grandfather's watch at such moments. That was all very well she told herself but it still didn't excuse two weeks fishing at beginning of term. Fishing in the mountains indeed.

R ALPH SUTHERLAND was not at all as Marie had expected. Of medium build and thick shouldered, he looked the typical forest man, not given to hasty movements. He had Tommy's same dark brown eyes and he had a disturbing habit of staring boldly at Marie as he spoke.

"So you're the new teacher," he greeted her, examining her from head to foot. He relieved her of her duffel coat, shaking it deliberately on the veranda to remove particles of snow then carrying it inside to hang beside the fire.

Now, in the warmth of the timber house she could feel her cheeks tingle and glancing at a mirror on the wall, Marie noticed that her hair still held a dusting of snow but this was melting quickly into droplets of water which ran down her face.

"Here," called the man, tossing a hessian towel in her direction. "Give it a good rub then we'll eat."

He was so down-to-earth she could not take exception to his command.

"Now," he held out a chair for Marie to sit opposite him and told Tommy to bring out the casserole. Marie watched as the boy moved to the stove beside the open fire, unhooked with a cleek the hot door and bent over. The boy came out with an enamel dish draped in a towel and set it ceremoniously on the table.

"I hope you like venison," Ralph Sutherland said as he proceeded to serve it up. The meat was flavoured with herbs and served with carrots and courgettes soaked in a rich gravy. On her sideplate Marie found a heel of a warm loaf and decided she felt ravenously hungry.

"Well," said Ralph Sutherland, as he watched Marie wipe the last smear of gravy from her plate. "Tell me the worst. What has my scallywag been up to this time? Last year Miss Wimple was for ever sending notes along with Tommy, but I must admit she never ventured through the forest to tick me off."

As he spoke, the man reached out a hand and ruffled his son's hair. It was an affectionate gesture completely cancelling out any sting or reprimand. In the light of this, Marie felt lost for words. Beside this, it was difficult to complain about someone's behaviour after one had partaken of such an excellent meal.

"I suppose it is because I took my boy fishing after the autumn break," he now forestalled Marie. "Well of course the summer holidays are such a busy time for us up here. I can never manage a break with the boy, so I take the chance when I can. You surely don't object to a father spending a bit of time with his boy?"

29

WHAT could she say? The man's words made perfect common sense. They were a truly remarkable pair, talking together man to man. Now Marie knew where Tommy had learned his deliberate ways. The boy gave a fairly accurate breakdown of his day at school including the rescue of the toad. Ralph nodded his head approvingly as Tommy recounted his action.

At last, however, Marie was able to have her say.

"To say the least, Mr Sutherland, Tommy's work is temperamental, as is his time-keeping."

The man grimaced.

"I remember I was pretty hopeless at figures when I was at school, too, and I know the boy's spelling is a bit dicey, but I have to say I rather enjoy reading his wee stories."

Marie did, too, she wanted to tell him. Just that afternoon she'd read Tommy's ink-splattered exercise in reply to her demand that he describe "a typical day in his life."

"Today I found some hare tracks in the snow," the boy had written. "The marks they made looked just like my grandfather's watch-chain."

Ralph was absolutely correct, of course. One couldn't help being fascinated by Tommy's descriptions.

"He has a good turn of phrase," she admitted now, "but oh dear, the spelling, and you know, Mr Sutherland, one has to learn the mechanics of language before one goes experimenting."

In Times Of Trouble

IF fate has been unkind to you
   The tears will often flow.
Don't be ashamed, just let them fall,
   It's nature's way you know.

But do remember other folk,
   They have their troubles too.
Just do your best, and look around
   For something you can do.

Some kindly deed to bring relief
   To others who are sad.
And though it's hard, in time
   You'll feel that life is not so bad.

For troubles shared are troubles halved
   At least that's what folk say.
They're right, you know,
   You'll find the sun will shine again one
   day.
                    — *Irene Bernaerts.*

"Rubbish," broke in Ralph. "A lumberjack doesn't need to learn the name of each tree before he cuts it down. He'll learn along the way."

Marie spent two happy hours arguing with Ralph Sutherland whilst they roasted chestnuts on a tin platter above the open fire. Marie would blow on the hot flesh before sinking her white, even teeth into the nut and when she'd look up it was to find his dark eyes watching her.

In between their arguments, Marie learnt how Ralph's wife had died when young Tommy was just three and how a series of housekeepers had spent varying numbers of months tending their needs.

"Invariably," Ralph sighed, "they grew tired of the isolation and scurried back to town. You won't run away, will you, Marie?" he challenged her now, and she felt her cheeks burn.

Marie suddenly realised how at home she felt in this man's house and how comfortable it was sitting by the fire. The arguments were stimulating, Marie sometimes scoring points, then at other times agreeing that he did have a point. Her attitude to teaching would never be the same again, she told herself. Like the trees in Ralph Sutherland's forest, she would have to learn to bend with the wind.

IT was eight o'clock before she finally prised herself out of that cosy armchair and Ralph insisted upon walking her home. Occasionally he would touch her arm and point to some wonder of nature. Marie felt eager to learn. She too, it seemed, had grown hooked on his winter wonderland.

"I can see the lights from the schoolhouse," she told him eventually. "I should be able to see my own way home now."

He wouldn't hear of it.

"There's a tricky bit just past the row of oaks. He held aside a branch for Marie to slip under and just in time, too, for a moment later she felt her feel sliding on ice and his thick arm snaked round her waist.

"Steady now," he told her simply and Marie heard herself reply primly.

"Thank you, Mr Sutherland."

"Ralph," he pointed out accusingly. "We're much too small a community for such formality, Marie."

"Ralph then," she allowed, "but really there's no need for you to come further. The lights are perfectly clear now."

"Goodness. Did you see that wildcat over there?" he asked suddenly and Marie jumped almost a foot in the air, and quickly agreed to him walking her right to the schoolhouse door.

Inside the porch she turned to look at him. He was still watching her with his dark brown eyes. She imagined she caught a glint in them and drew back quickly.

"I wouldn't dream of it," he told her now.

"Dream of what?" asked Marie naïvely.

"Why, kissing the school-ma'am on the first night I walked her home, of course. But that's not to say there won't be other occasions."

Marie spun round and ran towards the front door turning the handle quickly and letting herself in, but she could hear his gentle teasing laugh long after he'd marched back into the forest.

For a long while that night Marie lay in her bed in the attic gazing up at the skylight, watching flurries of new snow blow against the pane, and she wondered if the man had stopped to watch any haretracks in the snow on his road home again, and if he thought about her, too, when he got there.

Marie went to sleep with the smile still curving her lips and dreamed of watch-chains and black crows, chestnuts roasting on the fire and about a man called Ralph Sutherland. □

TWO'S COMPANY...

I LOVE you, Carol, I want us to get married soon — now."

"But we've nowhere to live, love. You know how expensive furnished rooms are, and the council lists are miles long. We need time to save up for a deposit on a place of our own."

"That takes years!" Mack Holt frowned.

Carol and Mack had met on the Newcastle industrial estate where they both worked. He was in the office of a biscuit factory and shared a modest room in the city with his mate. Carol made up dolls' clothes in a small company called Toys and Things, and shared a rather dark, basement flat with two other girls. Mack was a true "Geordie," but Carol had come across the Border from Kelso, her home town.

"There's just a chance our basement might be free by Christmas . . ." Carol said now.

by LAURA CALDWELL

"It's not what I want for you, sweetheart, I don't fancy it myself," Mack replied.

They were very much in love and didn't want to wait until Christmas. Then Mack came up with what he called his "brilliant idea."

"There's one way we can have a roof over our heads and save too — move in with my mum and dad!"

But Carol wasn't convinced.

"Two couples sharing a house seldom works, love."

"But we'll both be out all day. We can make our late meal in the evening when Mother's done with the kitchen. The house is big enough. It's all so simple."

"But what will your parents say?"

"They'll be really chuffed. They're getting older. We'll help to keep them bright."

So Carol and Mack were married a month later on her nineteenth birthday. And moved in to number seven Lake Road.

"You and Carol can have your old room, son," his mum said. "Put in a couple of comfy chairs and a wee table and it'll make a nice little bed-sitter just for yourselves."

"This is a bit of a turn-up, isn't it?" Mack's father Bob muttered to his wife when they were alone.

"Well they were so keen to get married, dear, I didn't like to say no." Brenda Holt sighed. "We've plenty room."

"Aye," shot back her husband, "sometimes too much!"

But by the time the chairs and a coffee table and a selection of the wedding-gifts were installed the bedroom began to look something like a furniture store. Never mind, it meant no more agonising partings after dates. It was to be their own little love-nest.

HOWEVER, with the onslaught of a Newcastle winter the love-nest turned out to be chilly.

"This wee electric heater isn't nearly enough," Carol shivered and Mack agreed.

So gradually, the newly-weds dispensed with the bother of carrying their own meals upstairs.

"It's just plain daft!" Mack decided. Soon they were sharing his mother's good cooking, the living-room fire, and the colour telly with Mack's parents and his elder brother Frank.

Frank Holt was twenty-four. He came and went in the family house. He had set his heart on a career as a jazz musician and he played the saxophone in a group called Crazy Silver but so far, Crazy Silver had not been overwhelmed with professional engagements.

Therefore when Frank was "resting" between dates he settled back in number seven. Sometimes the group came along to Lake Road for a whole-day rehearsal.

"It jogs up the old folk, keeps them cheery," Frank told himself seriously.

"If that's music then I'm the king of the Cannibal Islands!" his father had been heard to mutter. And he would stalk away to his den, adding,

"The sooner I get word from Mooney, the better for us all."

His wife was disturbed. Bob was a man of few words, always had been, and she wondered if it was possible he was becoming a little bit "strange" since he retired from his busy days at the shipyard. Who was this Mr Mooney?

It was not as if Bob was ever at a loose end. He had his hobbies. One was his rose garden, the other his schooners. When summer and flowers were at an end he moved indoors to his den in the utility-room to build model schooners with spent matchsticks. He would spread his kit over an old table, draw soothingly on his pipe, happy as a sandboy.

But now increasingly as the days went on Brenda would hear this muttering about the mysterious Mr Mooney. At last she plucked up courage to ask about him.

"Who is this man Mooney, love?"

"Just a friend, a very good friend, I'm waiting to hear from him . . . Brenda, have you seen where I put my new tube of glue, lass?" The abrupt change of subject was a message to his patient wife that he wasn't prepared to divulge any more secrets meantime.

But still she wasn't at peace.

"Do you know anything about Dad's Mr Mooney?" she asked her sons.

Frank shook his head.

"Never heard of him," said Mack.

A FTER Mack and Carol had been sharing his parents' house for about five weeks a blow fell for Carol. Toys and Things were threatened with closure. The manager called a staff meeting to explain the situation. It was a case of too few new orders, mounting bills, business just ticking over — it was a sad and too-familiar story.

"Sorry, folk, we'll have to make do on part-time, my job's at risk too," he announced.

Carol was offered work just four afternoons a week.

The day this news came she didn't go straight home to Lake Road. She called to see if her old friends were at home in the basement flat. Then she went to a nearby café and sat alone to think things over. Fancy having to be at home sharing a kitchen every morning with her mother-in-law! Mack's mum was nice, of course, kind and generous, still Carol didn't fancy spending so much time with her.

Then there was the question of her big drop in wages; it was hard enough trying to save for their own house with a full-time job. There were tears in her eyes that night as she and Mack got ready for bed.

"Look at it this way, honey," he comforted her, "how much worse it would be if we'd taken out that mortgage on a new house, or had to face a big rent for furnished rooms. That way we would be in bad trouble. But we're OK here, the old folk are really pleased to have us, keeps them alert."

"She can knuckle down and help with the cooking then, Brenda," said Bob Holt when he heard his young daughter-in-law would be working just part-time.

"In that case we'll all be living on burnt toast and Chinese take-aways! And you're the very one who wouldn't like that, Bob Holt!"

Brenda was amazed at herself for being so brusque with her dear old Bob. But honestly, did he not think she had enough to do these days without teaching young Carol how to cook!

She had to fight a surge of sheer irritation, all the help her husband was lately was to mutter about this fanciful Mr Mooney.

ONE morning Carol was coming back after a spell in town window-shopping, when she saw a taxi draw up at the house. A little boy, followed by a trendy young mum carrying a toddler, got out. Goodness, it was Mack's sister Mavis! She hurried to help them into the house.

"Mavis!" cried her loving but astonished mother. "What is it? What's happened?" Mavis didn't often pay them a visit, her home was in Birmingham.

"Nothing's happened, keep cool. I'm just bored. Terry's gone off on one of his seminars for three weeks. I stuck it alone all last week then I took the notion to come up here to stay with you and Dad. I know you can't see enough of the grandchildren."

But we had our grandchildren for a whole month in the summer, Granny thought, dismayed.

"Where's Dad?" their daughter was asking. "Maybe he'll be a honey and fetch the cot down from the attic. Carol, you can help me take all this stuff up to my old room."

"But Frank's moved into your old room, Mavis. He's 'resting' between engagements so he's at home just now, and I let Mack and Carol have the boys' old room . . ." Brenda Holt felt a headache coming on. It was a real job and no mistake trying to please everybody.

"Well, Frank will just have to move out of my room, won't he?" Mavis said briskly.

"He's young, he can bed down on the couch or in the bath or whatever for a couple of weeks, surely."

There was a roar and a sound of scuffling from Bob's den. Bob emerged, red-faced, propelling his four-year-old grandson ahead of him.

"I've just been telling the lad he's not to lay a finger on his grandpa's matches — he managed to sweep six weeks' work on to the floor in one go!" And then, a little ashamed at his less than lukewarm welcome to his family from the South, he cuddled his pretty daughter close.

"Aye, Mavis, so you've come back home as well, love?" And Bob went off to climb into the attic to bring down the old cot muttering to himself: "If that Mooney man doesn't come soon I'll eat my hat, I will!"

A few days later, the young folk had all gone out to the pictures and Brenda and Bob were baby-sitting.

"News is coming on!" Bob called at ten o'clock to his wife, who was in the kitchen. There was no response and he strolled through to see what she was doing.

Brenda was spreading a pyramid of rolls with potted meat.

"I'll be through in a minute, pet," she said. "I'm just making up some supper for the youngsters. They've got such good appetites."

"You spoil your family, you always have done," her husband growled, and he went off to watch the news.

Maybe I do spoil them, thought Brenda in her anxious but gentle way, but surely Bob realised how lucky they were — the children could be scattered all over the world. She also reminded herself how lucky it was they had still such a roomy house since they were allocated number seven Lake Road by the council when their family was at the toddling stage.

It was a pre-war council house, very sturdily built but now lacking up-to-date fittings. A year ago the Holts had been given a chance to buy it. But to his wife's surprise Bob had firmly refused.

Brenda had not argued . . . it was possible Bob was right. If they bought the house they would never move again, and sometimes she dreamed of a bright new kitchen, no stairs, a coloured bathroom suite like her cousin Lily who had splashed out in avocado . . . Ah, well!

Now, having set a supper tray with the potted meat rolls, and some tempting cakes, Brenda went through to flop into a chair and watch the news. But the television had been turned off! And Bob was seated at the table, writing-paper

Nostalgia

I REMEMBER the kitchen, warm and
   wide.
Magnetically it drew the family inside,
So comforting, despite the fire emitting
   smoke,
An environment which wrapped us like a
   cloak.
The shiny black range held a stewing
   pot,
And the kettle sang as it sizzled hot.
There was a rug which could not hide
The threadbare sofa, where we sat side
   by side.

Now, visiting my children my eyes blink,
All appears cold — fridge, freezer and
   steel sink,
Where bubbles sparkle, float and fall,
And pretty patterned tiles adorn the
   wall.
Time is saved by washing machine,
Floor is bright, unworn and clean,
But nostalgia must go, it's useless to me,
My grandchildren can't visualise the way
   things used to be.
— Anne Peters.

spread out, pen poised, brow wrinkled, composing a letter.

Brenda struggled to get out of her seat to see what he was writing. But her husband waved her away.

"Sit down and rest your legs. It's just a bit of private business I'm working on. Stay where you are."

He completed the letter, placed it in an envelope, found a first-class stamp and announced he was just nipping out for a short time.

"But it's pouring cats and dogs, love!"

"I know, I know. But I must post my letter. It's for my friend Mooney and it's urgent." And with this Bob donned his coat and stepped out into the pouring rain.

THE following Saturday while Mother and Father were having breakfast — the young folk seldom appeared on Saturday mornings — the letterbox rattled. Bob was out of his chair like a shot. He came back waving an official-looking envelope. Carefully he tore it open, and Brenda noted his fingers trembled. He read the contents once, twice.

The next moment her sober husband leapt to his feet with a triumphant shout.

"It's from Mr Mooney!" He seized his bewildered wife and spun her into a crazy waltz around the breakfast table.

"It's happened," he sang. "Mooney's come up trumps at last! Get your glad-rags on, my bonnie lass, we're going out, you and me!"

At ten-thirty exactly Mr Mooney called and took the Holts off in his car. It wasn't a long trip, just down Lake Road, past the new supermarket, past the bowling green and community centre and round the corner into Chestnut Grove. In the pretty, leafy cul-de-sac six small, new houses stood in a semi-circle — miniature bungalows each with its own front plot and chestnut fencing.

"Mr Mooney is the housing manager for the council!" Bob revealed to Brenda in a proud whisper. They drew up at number three and Mr Mooney, a shining new set of keys clinking in his hand, motioned his passengers to follow him.

"I must say the council's done the city proud this time," Mr Mooney enthused, as he took them on a conducted tour. "Neat little houses these, one bedroom, a sitting-room, a small kitchen and a bathroom with a turquoise suite."

Brenda was enchanted.

"We're building this type with folk just like you in mind," the housing manager continued, "family off their hands, want something smaller, easier, quieter. You have been the best of tenants, Mr and Mrs Holt, for many years in our Lake Road estate, so when you came to put your names down for something smaller I saw to it you got top priority."

"And I never knew you put our names down, love!" Brenda exclaimed.

"Oh, it was over a year ago — when we got the chance to buy the family house, mind? I thought about it, then I said, 'no, no, Bob lad, you stick with the council and see what they come up with next.' I went off and had a talk with Mr Mooney here, after that it was just a case of waiting.

"I did it for you, pet," he told Brenda later. "I wanted to see you with a smart, new kitchen and just room enough for the two of us."

"Bob, what about the family?" His wife looked a little worried.

"No problem; they'll be welcome to come for high-tea every Sunday if they want."

"But — what if they want to stay, Bob?"

"Again, no problem, they can bed down in wigwams all around our front plot — that is if Mr Mooney will give his permission!"

Mr Mooney laughed heartily at such absurdities.

"Shall we say a move in six weeks then?" He took out his official notebook and fixed his glasses.

"Suits us," said Bob.

When they all heard the astounding news, Mavis stayed on for another week and helped her mum clear out cupboards and drawers.

"You'll just have to come to Birmingham and stay with us now," she told them as she kissed them goodbye.

Frank Holt suffered such a shock when he heard the old home would be no more, he scurried off one night and took a job — live-in — as a barman-entertainer in a local hotel.

"It'll do till the Crazy Silver get their big break," he consoled himself.

"Six weeks to find a place of our own, Carol! It can't be done," his brother, young Mack Holt, groaned.

"It *has* been done, love. I can tell you now, the day I lost my full-time job I went round to see my old flatmates, but they'd moved away! So the basement's to let again . . . sorry, the agent insists on calling it a 'Garden Flat.' I signed up for it on the spot, used my savings to pay the first month's rent — we can move in two weeks from now."

"You're a treasure, sweetheart, old fashioned as paint and as wise as the three monkeys." Mack wrapped Carol in a loving bear-hug. "And I love you, love you, love you!"

"It'll work out fine," said a breathless Carol. "After all, living in a garden flat, you can only move up in the world!" ☐

39

I'M *not* desecrating our savings!" I protested hotly. "What a ridiculous word to use. You're making a fuss about nothing.

"I'm making a fuss about two hundred pounds!" Derek retorted, his blue eyes flashing fire. Two hundred pounds towards the business we're going to set up, and you want eighty-five pounds for a dress! Do you realise two hundred pounds brings in about twelve pounds a year in interest?"

I wanted to shout "So what?" but I didn't. Instead I tried to be reasonable. "It's part of my job, don't you see? Mrs Berrisford's going

by GAY WILSON

A QUESTION

40

to lend me the rest of the clothes, but I must have something special to wear in the evenings, for the après-ski parties."

"Après-ski parties," Derek scoffed. "You told me the trip was a perk because Mrs Berrisford is pregnant and can't go."

"So it is. I get my air fare, my hotel expenses and everything except special clothes. Mrs Berrisford has lent me her anorak and ski pants, but I haven't got anything for the evenings. I have to socialise, I have to really live the holiday so that I can write it up for the brochure. Surely you understand this?"

OF PRIORITIES

Derek gave a deep sigh and ran his hands through his thick brown hair. "Well, it was your idea to save so stringently. You said you wouldn't mind if it meant we could get married that much sooner."

"You're not even trying to understand," I interrupted, "This is special. I've slaved away in that stuffy travel agency for three whole years, and if Mrs B. hadn't become pregnant, I wouldn't have got this chance. I *thought* you'd be pleased."

"It's purely a question of money," said Derek. "Hard-earned savings being frittered away on a silly outfit."

I really saw red then. "Whose savings are they?" I demanded. "You haven't contributed much for the last twelve months. You know very well you haven't!"

He went white at this and his eyes darkened in anger. I wished I could have withdrawn the unkind words, because I knew why he hadn't been able to save. It was his fees at the Commercial College — but it was too late now.

"I'm sorry about that," he said stiffly. "I thought we had an agreement."

WE stood and glared at each other then, neither willing to climb down. If he had taken me in his arms and uttered one word of love, I would have given up all thought of the trip. But he didn't. He just stood there, flushed and angry, and in a moment of sheer impulse I tore off my engagement ring and flung it on to the hearthrug.

It was a gesture of petulance and frustration more than anything else. I didn't really mean it, and I stood waiting for him to pick it up and coax me to put it back on, but he didn't! Instead he reached up to the mantelpiece and lifted down the model cottage with the slotted chimney pot where we kept our joint savings. Then, quite deliberately, he lifted the hinged roof and scattered the notes and coins on to the rug beside the ring.

"You'd better help yourself," he said coldly. "As you've told me, it's mostly yours anyway." With that he walked out of the room.

I waited until I heard the front door click, and then I collapsed on to the hearthrug and indulged in a storm of weeping. It wasn't fair! I was sick of scraping and saving. It was no fun any more. I was sick of every single one of my clothes. Sick of watching TV night after night because we couldn't afford to go out.

I hated that silly money box, too — stuffing every pound we could spare down its grasping chimney. Derek said it represented our dream home. Dream home! His, not mine!

Why shouldn't I indulge in one small flutter before settling down for good? In any case, it wasn't a flutter. It was a job of work, along with a perk, of course. I'd noticed how the sparkle had slowly gone out of Mrs Berrisford when her Simon had lost his job, and now she had to leave hers because of the coming baby.

"Don't get tied down too soon, Sue," she told me. "I wouldn't change Simon for anybody else in the world, but sometimes I wish we'd waited a bit longer before taking on so many commitments."

A Question Of Priorities

AFTER I'd made my face look like nothing on earth with weeping, I picked up my ring and the money and counted out exactly eighty-five pounds. Then I put the rest back in the model cottage and returned it to the mantelpiece with the ring hidden behind it. I hoped Mum and Dad wouldn't notice I wasn't wearing it and start asking awkward questions until Derek and I had decided what was to be done.

I knew they'd be very upset if I told them we'd broken everything off. They thought the world of my fiancé. I did too, of course, but there were times when he could be positively obtuse, and this was one of them.

I remember hovering round the phone for the rest of the evening, but he didn't ring, and I went to bed full of resentment, tossing and turning until the early hours of the morning.

The next day, coldly resolute, I told my boss I'd accept the assignment the moment I got into the office (before I could change my mind).

"I'm really glad about this, Sue," he said. "You're young for the job, but you've got your head screwed on and you have a real flair for reportage. Now, I want you to enjoy this trip, take advantage of everything that's offered, just as though you were a tourist. Then you can write it up in real glamour terms. Advertising is our life blood, as you very well know."

After work I went straight to the Modiste's shop where I had seen the winter sports wear. I hoped desperately she hadn't sold the après-ski dress and could hardly wait to get inside the shop. I was lucky — although it had gone from the window it was still on the rail, and in my size, too.

"It's perfect." The salesgirl sighed wistfully, as she zipped me up. "Are you going winter sporting?"

I felt like somebody from another world as I nodded, naming the place in the Alps where I would be staying.

I HURRIED home with my precious package, and hid it at the back of my wardrobe. I knew I'd show it to Mum later, but just at the moment guilt overshadowed my pleasure, and I knew the moment of glory had to be postponed.

"Is Derek coming round tonight?" Dad wanted to know as we sat round the table having tea.

I felt myself go red. "No," I muttered. "We're meeting at the Badminton Club. He's playing in a match."

I mumbled something and escaped. I was trembling inside at the thought of meeting Derek again. What sort of attitude would he take? It was the first real row we'd ever had, and I couldn't imagine how we were going to make it up, especially as I had decided to go ahead with the trip and spent the money on the dress.

But Derek didn't show up, which was unheard of for someone playing in a match. The secretary didn't seem concerned, however, so I guessed he must have received some sort of message. Every time the door opened and somebody who wasn't Derek came into the room, I was filled with a hollow desolation.

Every instinct in my body urged me to get on to the phone to him, but I fought it back. There was a principle at stake, and I was determined not to give in. In any case he'd ring me the following day, he always did on Thursdays — our night for going to the library together. (Another cheap night out, I thought, deliberately fanning my resentment.)

But he didn't ring, and I spent all day making mistakes on my typewriter. It was awful, and after tea that evening I blurted the whole miserable story out to Mum.

"Perhaps you *should* ring him, Sue," she suggested gently. "After all, eighty-five pounds is a lot for a dress."

"I can't ring him!" I wailed. "I can't! You do see my point of view, don't you?"

"I see both points of view," Mum said. "Only too clearly."

"I'll pay it all back," I said miserably. "Every penny. I've made up my mind to do this. I want money instead of presents for Christmas and my birthday from now on."

"Well, cheer up. Things have a way of working out and worrying

GREAT BRITON

LIVINGSTONE AND STANLEY

Famous Scottish missionary and explorer David Livingstone was born in 1813 in a tenement building in Blantyre, Strathclyde. Now the Livingstone National Memorial, the house contains a collection of his personal possessions.

Travelling extensively in Africa, Livingstone was the leader of the expedition which discovered Victoria Falls and the Zambesi.

Sir Henry Morton Stanley, born in Denbigh, Wales, in 1841 was a journalist and also an explorer. In 1871 he was sent to Africa by the New York Herald to find Livingstone. Together they explored the northern area of Lake Tanganyika.

won't help. In any case, now you've given your word to Mr Richardson,
'you'll have to go. Perhaps Derek will find out the time of your plane and
turn up at the airport.''

But he didn't and I had to set off with only Mum and my young
brother to see me off.

I CHEERED up a bit once we were airborne. I'd never flown before,
and the sensation was exhilarating. All of a sudden my troubles
seemed to float away and I experienced a glorious freedom. I told
myself I was about to begin the most exciting adventure of my life, and I
wasn't going to miss one moment of it.

"Lake Geneva's just below us," the pilot announced as we flew over
the snow-capped Alps and I peered down at the sparkling stretch of
water amidst the snowy peaks, shuddering with a tiny thrill of fear.

There was quite a party of travel agents gathered in the hotel, and
soon we were chatting together at the bar. I felt terribly inexperienced
and shy, and one of the women, called Roz, made a point of being nice
to me. "You're very young." She smiled. "Is this your first assignment?"

I found myself telling her about Mrs Berrisford and how I had been
chosen to take her place at very short notice. "I have to do well," I
explained, "so that I can write it up for our new brochure. There's an
awful lot at stake."

"Well, join us on the beginners' slopes in the morning." She smiled.

Mrs Berrisford's scarlet and black ski outfit fitted me very well. She
must have been extremely slim before she became pregnant, I thought,
and felt very much in the picture as I lounged around with the rest of the
party waiting for our instructor to arrive.

"If it's Sigmund," Roz told me, "you'll need all your courage. He's
the most ruthless man I've ever met. He terrifies beginners, but he's a
wonderful skier and absolutely dedicated to his sport. Don't let him
bully you though." She left me then, having been transferred to the
intermediate slopes.

It *was* Sigmund, and he was fantastic looking. His face and hands
were tanned to the shade of new leather, and his smile was a flash of
soap-powder whiteness which was devastating. When he pushed up his
goggles for a few minutes, I could see that his eyes were steely grey and
utterly cool, his features strongly Teutonic. I felt quite confident as Roz
had warned he could be ruthless, and I was determined not to be
intimidated.

Somehow, I managed to put up quite a decent performance or else
the rest of the beginners were too nervous to obey instructions, for he
came up to me afterwards and said, "This is not your first time ski,
nein?"

I don't know what made me lie, perhaps it was the exhilaration of
early success, but I nodded vigorously and agreed that this was not my
first ski!

"Bend more ze leg," he instructed, adjusting my position with a
gesture which made me sharply aware of his beautiful hands, "and keep
ze shoulders . . . so . . .''

ROZ was doubtful about my so-called success. "Well, watch it," she advised. "That Sigmund would sell his granny to further his career, and he's just opened his own ski school across the valley. Don't let him use you."

But I was too far established on Cloud Nine to pay much attention to my new-found friend. "I'd do anything to get the Beginners' Medal," I said, and Roz sniffed. "I believe you'd risk your neck to inflate your ego, and I'm quite sure friend Sigmund would."

The euphoria lasted, for it comforted me to take risks. I suppose it was my state of mind. If Derek didn't love me any more, nothing mattered. It was stupid, I know, but there it was. I had to put up a cheerful front when I was with the rest of the party, and it was only in bed at night that I allowed myself to *feel*. Then I was desolate, for I was sure that everything was finished between the two of us. I would have given anything to be able to put matters right . . .

There was no doubt I was in favour with Sigmund. After my fifth lesson and bits of extra practice when the others had staggered wearily back to the hotel, he told me he was going to transfer me to the intermediate slopes the following week, and I forced myself to work harder than ever so that I wouldn't disappoint him. I think I was becoming infatuated with him at this stage, for in my eyes he was indeed Superman — and I was hurt and sore and lonely.

I'd been on the intermediate slopes for two and a half days when disaster struck. Somehow I must have twisted the wrong way, for all of a sudden I was flat in the snow with my skis doubled up underneath me. He was beside me in seconds and I nearly swooned with delight when he gathered me up in his arms as though I was a feather, but I howled in agony when he set me upon my feet.

"My ankle!" I moaned. "I'm sure I've broken it." I remember sinking back into the snow and felt sweat running down my face despite the frosty air.

He was brisk and businesslike. "We get you to the first-aid post, *nein*?" he said calmly. "They fix things for you." But they didn't. They despatched me forthwith to the cottage hospital in the valley, and before I knew what was happening, my leg was encased in plaster right up to my knee.

Apparently I had broken my ankle in two places and I was told there was no likelihood of being back on my feet for two to three months.

It was almost too much to bear. Sigmund didn't even come and see me. Roz did, on the day the whole party were off to the Ice Carnival that same evening, which was one of the highlights of the trip.

"I did warn you," she said, dumping a bunch of grapes on my locker, which wasn't any help at all.

When she'd gone I stared out of the window at the great caterpillar contrivance which was grooming the pistes outside the hospital grounds, for there had been a heavy fall of snow the night before. I had plenty of time to think, and later as a veil of pink sunset slowly spread over the glistening peaks, my heart sank with the sun.

Here I was on my very first assignment which had cost me so dear and which I had completely messed up. If I hadn't boasted to Sigmund that I was much more experienced than I really was, I wouldn't be in this predicament. It was my own fault entirely, and it hurt me deeply that he hadn't even got the grace to come and visit me.

I hoped Mum wouldn't be too upset by the message I'd sent advising them of my earlier return home on crutches. I knew she'd be upset, but she'd make the best of it, and oh, what a comfort to have somebody to love and care for me again.

I buried my face in one of my huge feather pillows and had a real good weep. When I awakened it was dark and little twinkling lights on the lower slopes of the mountains winked and flashed through the clear air.

"A visitor for you, Fräulein," announced the little Austrian nurse putting her blonde, braided head round the door. Her eyes were twinkling. "Very 'andsome!" she added mischievously.

I reached for my comb and mirror hastily. So, he'd thought better of it and had come to see me after all. Perhaps he wasn't quite such a rat! I dabbed a smudge of powder on to my nose and outlined my lips. Then I sat back against my pillows and endeavoured to look pale and interesting.

B UT it wasn't the ski instructor who walked into the room. I thought I must be dreaming . . . When my vision cleared I could see it was Derek.

"I had to come, darling. Don't say you're not pleased to see me. You'll need help getting home, and . . ." He stopped, looking miserable and anxious and completely exhausted.

I stretched out my arms. "I've never b . . . been so g . . . glad to see anybody in my w . . . whole life . . ." I sobbed, and in one bound he was beside me, crumpling my spotless counterpane with the weight of his body, and holding me so closely I couldn't breathe. But it was bliss. Sheer, unadulterated bliss to be in his arms again.

"H . . . how did you know?" I sniffed into the front of his jacket. "How did you get here?"

"First things first," he said cheerfully, pushing me back against my pillows but still holding my hands. "Your mum phoned me about the accident, and I got here by plane, of course."

"But . . . but . . ." I twisted the sheet between my fingers, fixing my gaze at the lights outside the window. "It . . . it must have made a dreadful hole in your savings . . ."

The melting tenderness in his eyes as he turned my face round gently, made me realise that despite my broken ankle and lost opportunity, I was the happiest girl in the world.

"Better a dreadful hole in my savings," he said, "than a dreadful hole in my heart."

Over his shoulder I saw the little Austrian nurse stop abruptly on the threshold of my room. She had a tray containing a cup of hot chocolate in her hands, but she turned without a word and stole softly away. She didn't know much English, but she knew about love! □

With A Little Help From A Friend

by ELSIE JACKSON

ERIN STEWART felt her temper rising as the
classroom door opened at twenty-five minutes past
nine and Laura Murray made one of her entrances. Chin
up, the blonde girl stalked across the room to her seat. Had she
been in a better frame of mind herself, Erin might have ignored
Laura's late arrival and continued with the English lesson. As
it was, she had had a particularly harassing morning with her
mother, and Laura's blatant impertinence was no remedy for
ruffled nerves.

"Stand up, Laura!" she said sharply. When the teenager had done so,
as noisily as she could, Erin went on, "Perhaps you'll be good enough to
tell me why you have arrived ten minutes late for my class."

Laura regarded her with grey eyes, hard as pebbles. "Haven't a clue,"
she said eventually.

How I'd love to slap that insolent little face, Erin thought, her fingers
tightening round the edges of her desk. She took a deep breath. "Well,
I'll tell you what, Laura," she said quietly. "You can come here in your
free period tomorrow morning, and write me an essay on the virtues of
punctuality."

The girl's mask slipped, and for a moment she almost looked the child

48

she was. "But Mrs Walton's holding the auditions for the play then!" she cried.

Erin felt a little surge of triumph. It wasn't often she managed to penetrate Laura's façade. "Too bad!" she said. "I shall have to tell her not to expect you."

"But Laura's after the part of Maria!" a pale-faced girl in the second-back row exclaimed. This was Lesley Drake, who followed the glamorous Laura around like a pet lamb. Erin suddenly remembered, then, some talk in the staff-room about Laura, with her fine voice, being a natural for the part of Maria in "The Sound Of Music." Her lips tightened a little more.

"No doubt there are other girls in the school with as much talent as Laura — and manners to go with it," she informed Lesley tartly.

She felt the murmur of disapproval that went round the class every bit as clearly as she heard it. Her heart sank. For the next thirty minutes she would have to combat scowls, veiled rudeness, and sulky silences from the two dozen fifteen-year-olds in her charge. What a way to start a November day!

WHAT a job! Why had she ever given up her newspaper work for this? Her mother had said she was a fool, and after six months in Hartington Comprehensive Erin was beginning to agree with her. "Heartbreak Comprehensive," that's what it should be called, she thought drearily, as she listened to a girl deliberately muffing the lines of a passage she had asked her to read.

Erin felt no more cheerful by the end of the day. Monday was notoriously difficult for every teacher, but on this particular one there had been troublemakers in every class she had taken. As she drove home, she thought ruefully of all the high hopes she had entertained while she was at training college.

A mature student, she had been lucky to have been given a place there — or so she had thought. She had been twenty-six when she had started her course. And now she was twenty-nine. "Almost thirty," as her mother had tactlessly pointed out that morning, "and not a man on the horizon!"

▶ *p52*

Of the many small fishing villages along the East Neuk of Fife, Pittenweem is perhaps the best known. Fishing boats leave the picturesque harbour for the rich fishing grounds of the North Sea and their catch is as fresh and tasty as you'll find. The harbour is surrounded by old stone-built houses, many of which have the characteristic orange pantiled roofs, found in abundance along this historic coastline. The square tower on the church above the harbour dates from 1592, fifty years after the town was constituted a Royal Burgh by James V. Today, the restored fishermen's houses, the wynds and the harbour are favourite subjects for painters and photographers.

D. McDougall.

PITTENWEEM, FIFE

Erin drew up at the traffic lights, her eyes clouded with the hurt she had felt at breakfast time. If she had been my real mother, would she have spoken to me like that, she wondered. Then her face flamed at her own disloyalty. Mum loved her every bit as deeply as a natural mother could have done. If anything, she had been loved too much! She had had a marvellous childhood with her adoptive parents, both of them journalists. She had been given the best of everything.

When Dad had died she could not have grieved for him more. And now that Mum was elderly, and having to battle against failing eyesight and arthritis, she ought to be patient with her. It was sheer frustration that made her short tempered and liable to say unkind things.

Then as Erin turned into Poplar Avenue, her eyes brightened. Her mother ought to have received her first Talking-Book today. The Talking-Book machine had arrived a week ago, and she had been waiting impatiently to use it. Mrs Blair next door had promised to come in and show her how to operate it.

"I'll never be able to wait until you come home from school," Mum had informed Erin.

That should have cheered her up, Erin thought, as she turned into their driveway. A voracious reader, Mum had been lost without her books, and had been thrilled when she had been told at the hospital about this marvellous service.

"Hello!" Erin called brightly, as she pushed open the front door.

"In here!" a disgruntled voice called from her mother's bedroom.

Whatever's wrong now, Erin wondered as she hurried through. Her mother was sitting in her chair wearing what Erin teasingly called her "fiddle face."

"Would you look at that mess?" she demanded irately, pointing towards the Talking-Book machine.

Erin saw a brown heap of tape spilling out of a large, black cassette. "Oh dear!" she exclaimed. "The tape's spilled. Don't you remember Mr Blair said that occasionally happened? He read the instructions out to us, when he was fixing up the machine. Remember? We must send the spilled tape back right away, and you'll get a replacement."

"I want no replacement, thank you!" her mother barked. "They can have the machine back. That gave me the fright of my life when it happened. I thought I'd broken it."

"Oh, poor old Mum!" Erin began laughingly. "Don't sulk! I'll take this down to the post . . ."

"I mean it, Erin!" her mother cut in loudly. "I don't want that machine! I've enough to contend with without being frightened out of my wits. Take it away!"

Suddenly Erin felt terribly tired. "I'm doing nothing until I've had a cup of tea," she said wearily. "Would you like one?"

"No," her mother snapped.

A S soon as Erin was safely in the kitchen, the tears she had been holding back began to roll down her cheeks.

"Oh, stop it!" she scolded herself. "What good is this

doing?" It was a full five minutes, nevertheless, before she was sufficiently in control of herself to wipe away the last of her tears. And just as she did so, someone knocked on the kitchen door. She opened it to find a young man in a red anorak standing on the step.

"I'm from the Talking-Book service," he announced with a smile. "I've come to see that the machine's working all right. I'm Bryan McColl."

"Come in, please," said Erin, smiling wanly. "You're just in time to take the machine away. My mother doesn't want it."

"Doesn't want it?" Bryan McColl's dark eyes widened in surprise. "But she can hardly have used it . . ."

"She hasn't," Erin admitted, telling him the story of the spilled tape.

Bryan began to nod comprehendingly. "Let me have a chat with your mother on my own," he suggested. "I'll change her mind."

"I doubt it," Erin said. But she showed the young man into her mother's room and returned to the kitchen to put on the kettle.

Ten minutes later Erin heard her name being called. She hurried through to find her mother sitting with a placid smile on her face.

"Erin," she said, "I'm keeping the machine. Bryan here has just been telling me about all the folk who use them who're a lot worse off than I am. The truth was I was really scared of damaging it. But he assures me it's very sturdy, and says I've not to be so daft."

"Not quite in those words." The young man laughed, seeing Erin's startled expression. "I've given your mum another book to listen to, until her next choice arrives," he explained.

"And that's just what I'm going to do now," Mrs Stewart announced, switching on the machine. "So you two can run along and have a cup of tea."

"You'll have a cup?" Erin asked the young man, as they went through to the kitchen.

"As long as it's no trouble . . ."

"None at all," said Erin firmly. "Please sit down. I'm so grateful to you. Mum really needs those books. But she can be so stubborn — she used to be such a bright, active woman, you see. She was a journalist, and now her life's very restricted."

Bryan nodded. "And what do you do?" he asked.

"I was a journalist, too," Erin told him. "Now I'm a teacher."

Bryan smiled at her over his cup. "You don't look like the teachers I

▶ *p 56*

ULLSWATER, LAKE DISTRICT (see over)

Nine miles long, Ullswater is one of the large lakes in the Lake District. At the north end, mountains partition the lake into three reaches.

Gowbarrow Park, associated with Wordsworth's famous poem, *Daffodils*, borders one side of the lake and Helvellyn rises into the sky from the upper end of the longest reach. Enclosed by lofty fells, the beauty of Ullswater is quite breathtaking.

J. Woolverton

ULLSWATER, LAKE DISTRICT

used to know," he remarked. "I hated school when I was young."

"Really?" asked Erin, thinking how the young man, with his dark curly hair and red sweater, brightened up the whole kitchen. He had one of those easy personalities with which you felt immediately at home.

H IS dark eyes became thoughtful now. "I don't suppose they took the time to find out about their pupils," he said. "That was half the trouble. I didn't have an easy time at home myself. I didn't get on with my stepfather. There would be rows at breakfast time, then I would arrive at school and find myself in hot water there. Teachers to me were just harsh voices and stern faces.

"You never thought that they might have problems themselves, because they didn't seem like real people. I often think that if they had softened a little, we might have had a better relationship. Folk like me, I mean. With difficulties. The lucky ones got on all right, of course."

Erin was silent for a few moments. "Well, you obviously turned out all right." She smiled. "A valued member of the community, one who can talk my mother into changing her mind!"

Erin poured out two more cups of tea, and their conversation became more general. Finally it touched on holidays. Bryan was off skiing in January.

"We don't go away now," Erin said, trying not to sound too regretful. "My mother finds it too harassing."

"But surely you need a break," Bryan said, "after a term of those terrible youngsters?" Erin couldn't tell whether he was serious or teasing her.

"Oh, I've lots to do," she told him. "Decorating, gardening. I haven't much spare time for holidays."

It was six o'clock before Bryan left, and the evening meal was half an hour later than usual. When Erin apologised for keeping her mother waiting, Mrs Stewart looked quite startled.

"I hadn't even noticed, dear," she said. "I was so engrossed in my book!"

As soon as the meal was over, Mrs Stewart disappeared again to listen to the next chapter, leaving Erin time for her own reflections. She had plenty of them, too. One way and another, Bryan McColl had given her food for thought.

A T five to ten on Tuesday morning Erin hurried into her classroom to find Laura Murray standing sulking by the teacher's desk.

"I'll need some paper if I've to write this essay, miss," the girl said as rudely as she could.

Erin took a deep breath. She was about to take a course of action that might completely undermine her authority with her pupils. On the other hand, if Bryan McColl's experience was anything to go by . . .

"Look, Laura," she said briskly and a trifle shakily. "Let's forget the essay. The truth is I was feeling a bit on edge yesterday morning, and I flew off the handle. My mother's very trying sometimes, you see. She's very arthritic now and her sight's deteriorating. She gets frustrated and

With A Little Help From A Friend

says all sorts of unkind things to me. And I'm afraid my resentment hadn't worn off by the time I reached school."

She had not dared to look at Laura while she was making her little speech. She dreaded the look of contempt she might see on that pretty face, the glint in those grey eyes as Laura thought what fun she would have relating this incident to her friends.

When the teacher did finally look up, though, it was to find a very startled schoolgirl staring at her. There was a moment's silence, then Laura said, in a voice quite unlike her normal, hard one, "Well, actually, Miss Stewart, I hadn't had a very good morning myself."

She swallowed hard, and looked at Erin doubtfully. Then, as though deciding she could trust her, she went on, "My wee brother's in trouble, Miss Stewart. He was seen shoplifting with his pals. I know he shouldn't have done it, but he's only seven. And my dad's so hard on him. It's his pal who's really to blame." Her voice broke and she stopped abruptly. This was a Laura Murray that Erin had never dreamed existed.

Impulsively she put a motherly arm round her. "Don't upset yourself, dear," she said sympathetically. "Your brother's just one of the casualties of our modern age, I'm afraid. Most of the youngsters steal for bravado or to please a dominating pal. This fright's probably the best thing that could have happened to the lad. I'm sure he won't turn out a villain."

Laura gave a grateful smile. "Can I tell my dad what you said?" she asked.

"Of course." Erin smiled. "And now run along to your audition. I've a feeling Mrs Walton will be waiting for you."

THAT afternoon as Erin was leaving the staff-room to go home, she found Laura and two of her gang waiting anxiously in the corridor. Laura was the one who stepped forward.

"Miss Stewart," she began eagerly. "We just wanted to say that if you ever want to go out any evening, we'd come round and sit with your mother."

"Yes," Lesley Drake chimed in. "It might make a change for her, too. It's good for old folk to see new faces."

"The trouble is," said little Sheila Henderson, "they don't really feel old inside. That's what my grandpa says. You feel like you're twenty still, but your legs won't listen to you."

How wise they all are, Erin thought incredulously. And I've written them off as nitwits ever since I met them.

"Thank you very much indeed, girls!" she said warmly. "My mother doesn't really mind being left alone at the moment. But it's a great comfort to me to know I've people I could rely on, if I did need a sitter. I really mean that."

The girls beamed at her before they ran off. As she gazed after them, Erin knew that she would never have real problems with them again. They would doubtless have their ups-and-downs. But she finally established a good, working relationship with them — thanks to Bryan McColl.

HERE I am again." Bryan grinned, when Erin opened the door to a knock at six o'clock that evening. "May I have a word with your mother?"

"Why, yes," Erin said, feeling rather puzzled, but at the same time happy that the young man had called again. "The Talking-Book's working fine," she added hesitantly. "No problems."

"It's not about that," he said. "It's about something else that might interest Mrs Stewart."

"Go on into the living-room, then. She's sitting in there. I'm just making our evening meal, so I won't join you."

As Erin peeled the potatoes and scrubbed the carrots, she could not help being aware of the animated conversation that was going on next door. Now Bryan's deep tone could be heard, then her mother was talking excitedly. Whatever could they be discussing?

Mrs Stewart's cheeks were pink and her eyes bright when she called Erin through. "The most marvellous chance, dear!" she exclaimed. "Holidays for disabled folk like me in this lovely hotel on the west coast. Door-to-door transport. Beautiful accommodation, and all sorts of excursions while you're there. It's so reasonable too! Would you mind if I went?"

"No, of course not!" said Erin, looking as delighted as she felt.

"Perhaps there's a particular fortnight that might suit your daughter," Bryan put in hurriedly.

Erin gave a little gasp. Only that afternoon Mrs Walton, who was a widow, had asked her if she would be interested in two weeks in Madeira. She explained this to her mother, who nodded willingly.

"That would be fine, love," the older woman said amicably.

"I'll make the arrangements, then," Bryan promised.

Erin walked to the gate with him an hour later. He had been persuaded with no great difficulty to stay for a meal. It was a beautiful night, if a little frosty, with a star-sprinkled sky.

"I don't know how to thank you," Erin began.

"You could come out with me one evening," Bryan said promptly. "That's if you would like to, of course."

She looked up and found his eyes shining down on her, bright as the stars but much more warmly. Her heart gave a great, joyous leap.

"I would love to," she said simply. □

The War Memorial overlooks the bridge leading to Kelvingrove Park, one section of which contains the Art Gallery and Museum, the other being home for Glasgow University (seen here). The magnificent spire towering over this delightful park is 300 feet above ground. Founded in 1451, Glasgow University is one of Scotland's oldest and most important centres of education.

V. Bissland.

KELVINGROVE, GLASGOW

by JEAN MELVILLE

TIME FOR LOVING

CAROLINE KNIGHT could not believe her eyes when
she got home from work. She had spent the last part
of the day convincing a difficult customer that the new
hairstyle she had chosen would please her when she got used
to it.

Now, tired and hungry, she let herself into her grandmother's
small cottage then surprised, allowed her handbag to slide to the
floor — a large grandfather clock took up most of the tiny hall
and the hallstand had been moved into a corner.

Caroline had been living with her grandmother, Mrs Polly
Knight, for almost five months, ever since her parents had
emigrated to Canada, and she had decided not to accompany them.

She had been engaged to marry Lester MacDonald for over a year,
and they had no wish to be parted, but Lester had still to finish his training
before he could afford to get married, and they had both had a great deal
of saving to do.

It was Polly Knight who had offered the best solution. She had been
widowed for five years and had kept on the old family house, thinking
that her son and his family might like to live there one day. But when
Caroline's parents decided to emigrate, she had sighed deeply and
altered her own plans.

"All right, my dears," she had said gently. "This opportunity sounds
like a splendid one for you, Duncan, and Jenny is all in favour of it. But
I think I'll put my house on the market and buy a wee cottage. Caroline

can come and live with me if she wishes, until she gets married, then the cottage will be small enough for me to manage on my own. What do you think, Caroline?"

Caroline had thought it an excellent arrangement. She, too, was still in training as a hairdresser and she did not want to give it up.

O VER the next few months she and Polly, a small slender woman of sixty-four, enjoyed themselves house-hunting for the right cottage. When they found it they decorated and furnished it in a more modern fashion than the old family home.

Mrs Knight was sad when she had to part with her good old furniture, but she brightened up when she and Caroline moved into the cottage. It was warm, comfortable and easy to run. What more could she want?

As the weeks passed, Mrs Knight began to regret parting with her old wall clock. She had been used to its tick over the years and, unless she kept the radio on all day, the cottage always seemed very quiet after Caroline had gone to work.

Mrs Knight took to looking in the window of Pollock's, the auctioneers, and even began going in rather timidly once or twice, when a sale was in progress. Of course she would never bid for anything, she assured herself. But today a man had started bidding for an old grandfather clock and had almost bought it for eight pounds.

But it was worth *much* more than that, thought Polly Knight. It was a lovely old clock.

"Going at eight pounds . . ."

"Nine," she shouted.

"Nine I am bid . . ."

"Ten," said the man.

"Eleven," said Polly.

"Eleven I am bid. Lady in the back row. Any advance on eleven?"

"Twelve," Polly cried, her cheeks now rosy.

The other man chuckled.

"Madam, you are bidding against yourself," he said and, grinning, he bowed out in her favour.

Polly Knight found herself giving her name and address, and hiring a van to deliver the clock to the cottage. The delivery man helped her to move her coat-stand, and now the clock had pride of place.

She polished it lovingly, but although she wound it up with the rather ornate key, unfortunately it did not tick.

But that was no problem in their family, thought Polly, as she picked up the phone and rang Mitchell's the jewellers and asked them to send round their representative to mend the clock.

Then she hurried into the kitchen to prepare the evening meal for Caroline and herself.

M RS KNIGHT had not heard her granddaughter's arrival. She liked to do her cooking with the radio on to keep her company, and now she sang along with the latest pop songs as she worked away in the kitchen.

"Gran!" Caroline stared at her as she removed her coat. "What on earth . . . ?"

"Oh, do you like it, dear?" Polly smiled. "I bought it at an auction today. I miss some of my old furniture, you know, and especially my wall clock."

"But . . . it's *huge!* And what if it doesn't even work?"

"Don't you worry my dear, that's all been taken care of. I've rung Mitchell's, the jewellers, and asked them if they'd be able to send Lester round, officially. That way there's no fear of him mending the clock in his spare time. I want it all to be proper and above board so that he doesn't get into any trouble with his employer."

"You've done *what?* Oh, Gran!" Caroline could hardly keep the tears out of her voice. A week ago she might have been delighted with this news, but she and Lester MacDonald were not at present on speaking terms.

Caroline hadn't yet been able to talk about it to her grandmother, and had merely said that Lester was busy when she didn't keep her usual date with him the previous Saturday. And now this had happened!

"Oh, Gran!" she cried. "Please . . . not Lester! Not this evening!"

"It's the only time he is free this week, according to Mitchell's. He appears to be working very hard.

He must be making a conscious effort to save his money."

"Gran, I don't know what Lester is doing with his money, but it's not for our wedding. I should have told you, but I just didn't feel like talking about it."

Her voice broke into a low-pitched croak. "The wedding is off. We're not seeing each other any more."

Mrs Knight's eyes flickered and she stirred her gravy vigorously.

Who Am I?

I HAVE a little friend who follows me about,
He always goes where I go, when I am playing out.

He does all the things that I do, and never tries to hide,
When I walk, or run, or jump about he's always by my side.

He never says a word to me, although he's always there,
He's just as old as I am — in fact, we are a pair,

But when the sun goes down at night — it isn't quite the same,
Because my friend just disappears — can you guess his name?

— Dorothy Oldridge.

Answer: My shadow.

"There are lumps in this," she said, then looked again at Caroline.

"I'm sorry, dear, to hear it, but . . . well . . . young folk often have tiffs."

"It is *not* a tiff," said Caroline miserably. "It's very real."

IT had started in a small way when she had waited for Lester, as usual, in a small café near the salon. But after several cups of coffee, Caroline had been obliged to go home in the pouring rain without her umbrella, because she had expected to drive home in Lester's van. She had developed a miserable cold as a result.

She had understood that Lester had been obliged to work late. Mitchell's were cutting down on staff and Lester worked in the workshop during the day and did clock repairs in the clients' homes in the evenings. He was now fully trained and soon they had hoped to plan their wedding.

"Couldn't you have let me know?" Caroline had asked. "I could have caught the bus home."

"I did," he had told her. "I sent Doug."

"Well, I certainly never saw him!"

Doug MacDonald, Lester's young brother, had met some of his

GREAT BRITON

R. L. STEVENSON

Famed writer and traveller Robert Louis Balfour Stevenson was a native of Edinburgh. Best known for his classic adventure stories *Treasure Island* and *Kidnapped*, he also wrote a number of essays, letters, poems, fantasies and the macabre tale *Dr Jekyll And Mr Hyde*.

In 1888, at the age of thirty-eight, Stevenson and his family left for the South Seas. A victim of tuberculosis, he died in Samoa in 1894.

Edinburgh

friends and had completely forgotten his errand, and it was because of him that the row had escalated.

Caroline taught Doug in Sunday school and had a few things to say about his lack of attention. In reply Lester had defended his young brother, saying that he was a very normal boy for his age, but soon other small grievances were being aired.

When Caroline saw Lester's van a few nights later, with a very pretty girl in the passenger seat, she found it hard to believe that the girl was merely a customer and that they were uplifting a clock from her mother's home and setting it up in her aunt's.

"You're taking me for granted, Lester," she had accused him.

"And you'll hardly believe a word I say!"

"Then it's time we called it off," Caroline had cried, white faced.

"That suits me," he informed her, equally angry.

A ND now Gran had sent for him to come and mend her clock, thought Caroline miserably. As they sat down to eat their dinner together in the kitchen, she could only pick at her food and hope that Lester wouldn't come.

They had scarcely cleared away, though, when the bell rang and Mrs Knight hastened to welcome him in.

"You're just in time to join us for coffee, Lester," she said hospitably.

"Er, no thanks, none for me." Lester was uncomfortable.

Caroline wondered how she could gallop upstairs and hide in her bedroom. Her heart was sore and she felt like crying her eyes out when she saw his familiar, cheerful face, and his hair which always sported a tuft standing on end at the top of his head. How often she had smoothed it down for him!

"It's this grandfather clock," Mrs Knight was saying cheerfully. "I got it at a sale. My first ever, and I bid for it myself. But it won't go."

"Well . . . it *is* a bit neglected, Mrs Knight," Lester told her, as he spread out a cloth and began to take the clock to pieces. "Old clocks can be valuable, but they should be looked after over the years. I'll do my best with it, though."

"Fine, my lad." She smiled at him warmly. "Oh, I have to go out for an hour to see May Reid about our new china painting class, but Caroline will get you a cup of coffee when you are ready." She looked at her granddaughter. "I won't be long, dear."

The door had opened and shut before Caroline got her bearings, and a minute later she was in the house, alone with Lester. She had never been more miserable in her life.

It was her own fault for not talking to her grandmother earlier, she told herself.

"I'll be in here washing up," she said to Lester, stiffly, from the kitchen door.

"Oh . . . fine . . . fine." He was cleaning a great many parts and putting them back together again with an ease born of practice. Old Mr Mitchell had been an excellent watch and clockmaker, and a wonderful teacher, so Lester had received the very best of apprenticeships.

Caroline finished the washing up, then resisted the temptation to hang over Lester and watch him at work. It was no use, she thought, as a lump formed in her throat, she still loved him very much.

He was probably happy to be free of her, she thought miserably, remembering how happy he'd looked with that other girl.

Jealousy gripped Caroline anew as she did as many jobs as she could find in the kitchen.

"Can I wash my hands?" Lester's voice suddenly said from behind her, and she turned, startled.

"Oh . . . sure," she murmured. "I'll get a towel."

"No need — this one will do." He busied himself at the sink. "Er . . . how have you been?"

"Fine . . . great . . ." Caroline tried hard to sound natural.

"That's good, so have I. Everything is great. I might even have got that old clock ticking, but it's going to need new parts made. I can do that at the workshop, though."

"You're very smart," she assured him.

"I don't know about the chimes, though . . ." Lester rubbed his forehead, frowning.

SUDDENLY there was a strange, hollow rumble from the clock, and it began to chime loudly.

"One, two, three, four, five . . ." counted Caroline. When it reached fourteen, Lester began to look concerned. Then as the chimes went on and on, they chanted together:

"Thirty-two, thirty-three . . ."

Suddenly Caroline's lips twitched at the look on Lester's face and she began to laugh helplessly.

"Forty-seven, forty-eight," said Lester as he, too, began to laugh, and suddenly they were hanging on to one another as the clock chimed on, shuddering to a stop somewhere around a hundred.

"Oh, darling, I haven't been fine at all," Lester declared. "I've missed you so much."

"Me, too," Caroline murmured, her face nestling against his shoulder.

"It's only the strain of waiting to be married, you know. It was a quarrel over nothing, wasn't it?" He held her close to him. "I'll give our Doug a thick ear next time!"

"Next time I won't be complaining!" Caroline told him.

"Do you think your gran would give us that clock for a wedding present?" asked Lester a few moments later. "I'll really have to take the works back to my work bench, and start again."

"We start our married life without that clock," Caroline told him. "I've no idea why Gran bid for that old clock, but she can keep it! Just try to get it to tick for her."

Mrs Knight, however, knew very well why she had bought the clock, especially when she heard wedding plans being discussed as soon as she opened the door. □

Lost Moments

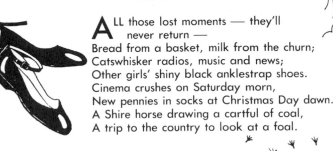

ALL those lost moments — they'll
    never return —
Bread from a basket, milk from the churn;
Catswhisker radios, music and news;
Other girls' shiny black anklestrap shoes.
Cinema crushes on Saturday morn,
New pennies in socks at Christmas Day dawn.
A Shire horse drawing a cartful of coal,
A trip to the country to look at a foal.

Pictures on tins of the Queen and the King,
Gas mantles fragile as butterfly wing.
Hopscotch and Yo-yos, a whip and a top,
A halfpenny to spend at Cameron's shop.
Swings and a maypole, sheds in the park,
Nightlight at bedside, fear of the dark.
Dandelion clocks, bluebells in woods,
Schoolgirls in colourful mac capes with hoods.

"Pilgrim's Progress" and Sexton Blake,
Tickets from trams, concertinas to make.
Codliver oil and malt in a jar,
Making a wish on a bright falling star.
Syrup of figs, toothpaste in tins,
Knitting a dishcloth on big wooden pins.
Blue bags of sugar, butter in slabs,
Sherbet and liquorice and caramel dabs.

Love hearts with messages, colours so bright,
Excitement in making and flying a kite.
Wrappers from oranges, cigarette cards,
Games played with friends in each
    other's yards.
We watched from a bridge as a horse
    pulled a barge,
Not knowing just then that the world was
    so large.
What is the mystery, why should it seem,
That those memories are clearer than the
    years in between?

— *June Picken.*

67

THE MAN FROM YESTERDAY

by ANNE MURRAY

WAS it really the very first night she had ever spent alone in a
house? As she sat in the comfortable lounge of the flat which had
been her home all her life, Kate Marshall found it a strange
thought. In all her thirty-eight years there had been someone here. If
her parents were away on an occasional holiday by themselves, there
was Granny, dear, cosy Granny, who was just like a third parent while
Kate grew up.

Now none was left. Granny had gone first, then her father, lastly her
mother, whose death had been sudden. Kind Mrs Smith, a neighbour,
had stayed with Kate then until her brother, Michael, came over from
Canada. He had been able to stay for two weeks, but this afternoon he
had had to leave to return to his home in Montreal.

So the loneliness that Kate had never known all these years was bearing
down on her now, filling her with a sort of apprehension. She began to
wish she had accepted her brother's suggestion that she return with him to
Canada. He was sure she could start a new life there.

"You could stay with us at first," he had urged. "Then we would find
you a place of your own, if that was what you wanted. I could get you a job
in our firm — staff keep leaving and have to be replaced. Do come, old
girl, you don't want to stay here alone for ever."

"I might come later on," Kate had told him, "but not just yet. There's a
lot to clear up, legal business as well, I think."

"Then be sure you do come later," Michael ordered. "In the
meantime, see and take advice from that lawyer chap if any problems
crop up. He seems very willing to help. In fact, I think he's got a notion for
you!"

"What nonsense!" Kate had retorted in annoyance. As if Gerald
Fenton saw her as anything but a client needing assistance!

For a few moments, she let her thoughts dwell on the young lawyer.
She liked and trusted him, knowing he was the same age as herself and

69

that he wasn't married. She'd learned these facts on the occasion he took her out to dinner — a pleasant outing, but one where quite a lot of business had been discussed.

Whatever could have made Michael think there was anything special between them? She recalled now how he had further annoyed her by going on to remark, "Yes, Fenton would be worth ten of that other fellow you once fancied." Then Michael had added something surprising . . .

"Funny thing happened the other day," he told Kate. "I bumped into Eddie Clarke near my office. I hadn't noticed him, but he stopped me and we had a bit of a chat. He asked after you, and if you had ever married, then he pushed his address at me, though I doubt if he'll be in Montreal long. He seems to be still drifting from one place to another, picking up a job when he can, that sort of thing. You were well rid of him, Kate."

NOW, sitting alone, she thought back across the years to the time when Eddie was one of the group of young people she knew. He had indeed been a drifter then, with no settled aim in life. But Kate had loved him, she hadn't minded that he never held down a job for long. She had given him her love and sympathy, and agreed to his wild plan that they should get married and go off to London to start a new life there.

She gave a deep sigh. Her parents had been horrified when they heard of this plan and Granny had wept copious tears. Kate couldn't stand against them, and at a farewell meeting she had told Eddie the engagement had better be broken in the meantime. She had promised to wait for him, and he had vowed he would love her always, and would come back when his fortune was made.

It seemed he hadn't done that as yet. But now in her loneliness, Kate felt a deep longing for those happy days of the past. She also found herself thinking of a story she had recently read in an old magazine.

The heroine in the story had been called Vera. She had been a plain, shy seventeen-year-old when she went around with a young man very like Eddie, who also had no proper work and not much purpose in life.

They also had decided to marry and the plan had been stopped by Vera's parents. Really, that story was uncommonly like her own one, Kate thought. Vera had gone on through the years and it was only when she, too, was left alone that she again saw the young man called Chris.

"Send for Chris," her father had whispered when he was on his death bed. So she had done that and Chris had returned. As soon as they met, Vera knew that here was her destiny. They married, and the end of the story was a year later when a little son had been born and they were blissfully happy. Chris was being kept firmly at the gardening work Vera had found for him, and he had settled down at last.

Kate's heart began to beat faster. Should she do what the young woman in the story had done? Should she ask Eddie to come back, try to find him a job, and ensure a life where she would never be lonely again? The more she thought about it, the more she liked the idea.

Eddie had asked for her, had asked if she had got married. So he still thought of her, and she had his address in Montreal. Michael had torn a leaf from his note-book, crumpled it up and thrown it in the waste-paper basket, saying he wouldn't bother making contact with Eddie when he got home again.

A moment's search through the basket revealed the torn paper, then Kate went to her desk. She usually kept a supply of air-letter forms with which she wrote to Michael and Lydia in Canada — yes, here was one.

She didn't write much, just that she had heard of his meeting with her brother, and wondered if his travels ever brought him to Britain.

"It would be nice if you came here some time," she had written, ending the letter with "Love, Kate."

WHEN she had sealed up the letter she sat dreaming for a moment. Would it all turn out like it did in the story? She felt sure it would. Eddie would come, they would take up where they had left off years ago, and marry. Like Vera, she would find him some sort of work, perhaps in the supermarket, where she was a supervisor.

The entryphone rang, making her jump. Who could be calling tonight? "Who is it?" she asked.

"It's Gerald Fenton. May I come up?" said the voice of her lawyer, who had been a tower of strength to her lately.

"Yes, please do," she replied.

Remembering what Michael had said, she felt her colour rise. She knew her visitor noticed as she greeted him at the door, but hoped her blush wouldn't give him the wrong idea.

"I remembered that your brother was leaving today," Gerald began, "so I guessed you might be missing him. At least . . . I wasn't sure if anyone would be with you."

It was kind of him to call in, Kate thought. Yes, it was very kind of him indeed. They chatted for a few minutes, then she went to make coffee. She had always felt at ease with Gerald, and how helpful he had been a year ago when her mother had wanted to make a new will. That was when she had met him for the first time.

"I've just realised this is the first night I've ever stayed alone in the flat," Kate said eventually.

Gerald looked worried. "Will you be all right? You won't lie awake feeling nervous, I hope?"

"I'll try not to be so silly." She smiled. "It'll seem strange at first, but I'll get used to it. After all, it must be harder for older people, who have perhaps been married for a long time, then suddenly one dies and the other is alone for the first time."

Gerald leaned forward and took her hands. "Kate," he said seriously, "you don't have to be alone for long. I didn't mean to say this quite so soon, but I think I've loved you since that day last year when you came into the office and we first met. Will you marry me, dear? I'm on my own, too, and I think we could be happy together."

Kate stared at him, confused. "Oh, no, no!" she exclaimed. "I didn't know . . . I never thought . . ." She stopped, deeply embarrassed, then pulled herself together. "You see, there's someone . . . I might be meeting an old friend soon. We were engaged once."

"I see," Gerald said with a touch of disappointment.

H IS eyes followed her glance towards the air-letter propped up on the mantelpiece, ready for posting, but he made no comment on it.

"What went wrong before?" he inquired with forced lightness.

"My parents didn't approve," Kate told him unwillingly.

"You feel now that they were mistaken?"

"I certainly feel that just because a man is a bit irresponsible at first, he can still be helped to settle down to a good, steady life," she answered defiantly.

There was a silence.

"What does he do?" Gerald asked at last.

Once again Kate knew she was blushing. She didn't want to admit that she had no idea, didn't even know if Eddie had any job at present.

"He's in Canada," she muttered. "Michael met him recently."

Gerald's face cleared. "Oh, well, if your brother knows about it . . . You think I'm merely being awkward, Kate, but you're my client, remember, and I want to look after your interests and make sure you're all right."

"If only my parents hadn't been so protective . . . ." Kate sighed. "I'm sure that getting married to me would have been the making of Eddie. It might still be. Anyway, I thought it right to let him know I was on my own now. More coffee?"

Gerald shook his head as he stood up.

"I'll go now," he said. "Will you let me meet your friend when he comes over? I expect you'll enjoy a reunion with him, but don't rush into anything impulsively."

"I'll remember your advice," she answered stiffly as she saw him to the door.

Whether she took it or not was another matter. It really wasn't his business to do any more than advise her on legal matters. She was old enough now to make up her own mind about anything as personal as marriage.

And what a surprise when he came out with that sudden proposal! It seemed Michael had been right in saying Gerald had a notion for her. She had never even guessed, for all they say that a woman always knew. He had looked so taken aback when she told him there was someone else.

A twinge of unhappiness shook Kate as she thought of his face when she rejected his offer. He looked really hurt and she didn't like hurting people for any reason, especially not a close friend such as Gerald Fenton.

R ESOLUTELY, she tried to put Gerald out of her mind — she must think about Eddie instead. Searching out some old photographs, she looked at the young man who had won her love years ago. He was so good looking then. Would he have changed? His dark hair might have grey streaks in it and he might have put on some weight. Yes, she must be prepared for some sort of change.

Here was a bundle of postcards which had come to her at long intervals across the years — brief, cheerful postcards from many parts of the world. She looked at one from Australia. "Trying my luck here," it said. "It's a great country, so I guess I'll stay for a while. Will be in touch."

But he hadn't stayed and he hadn't been in touch since that card from two years past. Never mind, it was just the same with that girl in the story. She also got postcards, and also hadn't heard for a long time when she at last sent for her Chris.

Next day, Kate posted the letter. Weeks of uncertainty followed when no answer came. She began to settle into a routine which was dull and which she hoped would not go on for ever.

Almost every week she saw Gerald Fenton. It was usually in his office to discuss some business matter or sign a document. Once, he called again at the flat. She got the feeling that he was keeping an eye on her, waiting to see if the friend from Canada really did come.

It was early one morning when Kate's phone rang. She left her breakfast to answer it, and when she heard Eddie Clarke's voice, her heart seemed to jump.

"That you, Kate?" he called. "I'm in London. I'm coming up to see you right away. There's a train every hour or so."

"Eddie!" She gasped. "It's wonderful to hear you. But I'm at work all day. If you come here about six-thirty that'll give me time to have a meal ready for you."

"Fine, I'll be there."

Kate stood motionless by the phone for several minutes. She felt strange. Her first thrill at hearing Eddie's voice had gone. Somehow the few words he had said weren't quite right . . .

He hadn't asked how she was, he hadn't said it was good to speak to her again, or how he looked forward to their meeting. Why did that seem to matter? The strange, uncertain feeling persisted as she sat and finished her breakfast.

Once again, she found herself thinking of that magazine story. There had been no preliminary phone call in it. Chris had just arrived on the doorstep and he and Vera had fallen right into each other's arms.

Well, things didn't always happen just as one expected. It would be all right when she saw Eddie. Kate pulled herself together and hurried to get ready for work.

IT seemed a long day, until at last she was free. Back at her flat she set about preparing the meal. Long ago, Eddie's favourite food had always been sausages and baked beans, so she'd give him that now. He'd be so pleased that she had remembered.

Everything was ready by six-thirty but he hadn't arrived. The minutes slipped away and it was nearly seven when the buzzer sounded.

"Eddie? Is that you?" She gasped.

"Sure thing," he answered. "Be with you in a second."

As she waited for him to come up the two flights of stairs, Kate felt her heart pounding. Once she saw Eddie, once she knew he was just the same . . .

She had known, of course, that he wouldn't look the same as when she last saw him, all those years ago. But for a moment she stared at him, unsure why he seemed so different.

His hair was still dark, if not quite so plentiful, and if he had grown fatter it was no more than she had expected. He looked so much older than a man not yet forty should be, and the happy-go-lucky expression she remembered was gone.

"Fancy you still living here!" was his greeting. Following her inside, he gazed round the room. "Comfortable enough," he went on, "but a bit out of date, isn't it? Well, no lift, for instance, just bare stone stairs, just like it was twenty years ago."

Oh, yes, Eddie had changed. He never used to be critical. Now he was looking at her closely.

"You haven't changed much either, Kate," he told her. "Dear old Kate, you were always the steady type who kept on the level. It's someone like you I need. I've always needed you, and it was a shame of your parents to part us. We'd have had a wonderful life together, wouldn't we?"

The scorn in his voice as he mentioned her parents jarred on Kate, and she hurried to get the meal on the table. They began with soup, then she brought in the sausages.

"Your favourite," she said as she put the nicely-arranged dish on the table.

"Sausages!" Eddie exclaimed. "Kate, you surely don't think I eat that kind of food now!"

He looked distastefully at the plate she put in front of him and began describing some of the wonderful meals he'd had in other countries.

"Well, never mind," he conceded. "You weren't to know. Kate, you really are marvellous. You don't expect anything to change. However, my dear, there's a big change ahead of you soon. You and I are going to get married, and I'll show you how to get some fun out of life."

There was nothing now to stop Kate marrying this man she had loved in the past . . . but more and more she felt it wasn't what she wanted. Eddie had changed too much. He wasn't what he had been, or else she had seen him then through the rose-coloured glasses of youth. Had her parents been right after all?

AFTER the meal, Eddie stretched out in an easy chair and regaled Kate with stories of the many places he had lived.

"I'm surprised you never got married," Kate found herself saying.

"Oh, but I did," he replied cheerfully. "Twice. It didn't work either time, so it's all in the past. I never forgot you, Kate, and when you wrote me, I knew this was it. I said to myself, 'Eddie, my boy, it's time for you to turn over a new leaf and settle down.' "

Just what she had planned to help him to do! But it shook her to hear that he had been married twice. Hadn't he promised to love and remember her always?

"What happened to your marriages?" she inquired.

"Couldn't stand being nagged at all the time," he told her airily. "You wouldn't go on like that, Kate, you're much too kind."

Kate took a deep breath. "Eddie, I can't marry you," she said quietly. "I think we've both changed too much. I'd rather just stay as I am. Or I might . . . I, er, might be getting married to someone else . . ."

Eddie sat up. "Someone else!" he exclaimed. "Then what do you mean asking me to come and see you? It was as good as saying you were free to marry me now, and wanted that."

"I only said come if you were ever in Britain," Kate defended herself.

But she felt guilty. She hadn't put much in her letter, yet when she wrote it she had meant just what Eddie said. Oh, dear, what a tangle she had got herself in. Wasn't it mostly because she had been thinking about that story and how similar some of it was to her own situation? What a fool she had been to think it was true and that her own life would develop in just the same way!

Eddie was angry and Kate realised he had thought that marrying her might well provide him with an income and a home for life. He would remember that her father's business had been a flourishing one, and that Kate would have independent means as well as what she earned at work. He said some unkind things which would have been much better left unsaid.

"Eddie, I'm sorry," Kate muttered. "Surely you could find someone to marry you who would be a better wife than the previous ones. If only you would find yourself a good job and stick to it, make new friends . . ."

"I've got masses of friends," he grumbled. "They like me even if you've turned against me. I never thought you would treat me like this, so I'll go. To think that I've just been filling in time till I knew you were free . . ."

SUDDENLY he seized her and began to kiss her passionately. If anything was needed to convince Kate that she couldn't marry him, this was it. She struggled, and at last he released her, a broad smile on his face.

"That was nice, wasn't it?" he boasted. "Oh, yes, Kate, we're meant for each other. So I'll be back."

"Please go now," she told him.

When he had gone, Kate went straight to the phone. She had never called Gerald at his home address before, but she soon found the number.

"Kate?" he queried. "Is anything wrong?"

"Could you come round?" she asked, aware her voice wasn't quite steady. "I'd like to see you."

"Now? Yes, of course."

It was good to see him, to look into his clear, grey eyes and see the concern in them as he asked what had happened.

"Eddie came," Kate said flatly. "He . . . he has changed. It wasn't his looks, it was just everything. So I sent him away, but he says he'll come back. I would like to be able to tell him . . . to tell him . . ."

"That you're engaged to marry me?" he asked gently.

Kate nodded.

"And after being engaged for a while do you think you might get to like the idea of being married to me?" he went on.

"I think, yes, I think perhaps I might," was her whispered reply. □

Return To Childhood Dreams

by JOAN ALISON

MURIEL JAMES stepped carefully over the tilting doorstep into the derelict cottage. Memories of idyllic childhood holidays came flooding back as she stood in the small space which she remembered as a chintz-curtained living-room. Funny how places seemed so much smaller when one returned to them as an adult. Perhaps it was a mistake to return at all to this remote part of the Highlands.

But it had become vital to come away in order to think things out. Murdo Forrester was a friend of her father's and had offered to find her a job in the computer firm where he worked. When Muriel's father had a stroke which robbed him of coherent speech, Murdo Forrester was kind and reassuring. She leaned on him a lot.

Now, she stared through the empty window opening at the sea. Waves broke gently on the shingle with a sighing sound as the water withdrew and gave way to the next blue-green curve. She almost expected to see her brother Robin run into the sea, daring it with Canute-like confidence to breach his sandcastle; to see her father digging with enthusiasm to rebuild the crumbling walls.

She'd been unable to explain to her parents the real reason for taking her holiday so abruptly, not saying where she was going, just when she seemed set for a successful career with Bailey's. But it was the state of affairs at work that had brought her here — a place where she'd been happy at a time when life was uncomplicated, before the nightmare began.

Murdo Forrester was a craggily handsome man in his forties. It was after her promotion to a small office of her own off the main complex that he implied Muriel owed him some form of recompense for his part in her advancement.

She was outraged, then thought she must have misunderstood and jumped to ridiculous conclusions.

77

He asked her to the theatre several times, then to a concert followed by dinner. No-one thought there was anything wrong in that. Everyone knew of the friendship between Muriel's father and the office manager at Bailey's.

Even when Murdo kissed her lightly on the cheek on parting, or allowed his hand to linger on her neck and shoulder when he helped her on with her coat, she thought nothing was wrong, had merely looked on him as something of a surrogate uncle, pleased that he had become fond of her. She protested about the small gifts he brought her — a box of chocolates, a flower for her frock . . .

Then came the veiled hints that, while he could help her to better prospects in the firm, he could also effect her return to the main office, even make it impossible for her to stay at Bailey's altogether. When she looked back on the previous six months, she couldn't understand how she had been so blind.

She dared not tell her parents, they had more than enough to bear. She took her holiday and said she had the chance to go away with a friend. An acceptable lie in the circumstances, she was sure.

NOW she turned away from the window and looked through the remaining rooms. There was a bag of tools in the corner and some lengths of wood. Someone had put down a new floor in the small back room where she and Robin used to sleep.

Rolled up in another corner was something that looked like a sleeping-bag, a camper's lamp and a couple of paper-backed books. She stooped to pick up the top one, curious to read its title and author, only to drop it abruptly as a voice spoke behind her.

"A thief caught in the act." A young man stood in the doorway, water dripping from his dark hair. "How far do I have to go from civilisation to be free from feminine curiosity?"

"I'm sorry. I didn't know . . . I was only . . ." But none of the clichéd responses fitted and Muriel wished she could sink through the newly-fitted boards. It served her right, of course. But there was no need for him to snap at her so rudely, was there?

He stood in the doorway, towelling his wet hair. Bright spots of anger flared in his cheeks.

"I've said I'm sorry," Muriel stammered and wished he'd move from the doorway so she could slip out and away.

"That's all you can say? No excuses pouring readily from your lips? Absolutely no justification?" He turned back into the main room of the cottage. "Good job I came in when I did. Goodness knows what you'd have walked off with . . ."

The mortification she felt at being surprised by this brusque man gave way to anger.

"Better repair the front door and hang a sign on it: *Trespassers Will Be Insulted.* And you'd better board up the door once I've gone. You never know. I might hide round the corner and sneak back . . ."

She stepped out over the doorstep and, without looking back, marched straight along the narrow path which wound up the hill towards the road.

Had she turned at the corner where the stream rattled over the boulders before disappearing through the tussocks of grass, she'd have seen the man leaning against the door-jamb, one corner of his mouth twisted in an amused smile.

That evening, in the house where she was staying, Muriel asked Mrs MacLeod about the old cottage at Drumore.

"You mean Tigh na Brahan? Oh, I hear that someone called Shaw has bought the lease. He's from Edinburgh way. They say he's going to write a book," she said scornfully, and laughed. "And I say it'll take him at least a couple of years to make the place watertight before he gets round to a book."

"When I was little we had holidays there. I remember paraffin lamps and carrying water from a dam built across the stream. We had to boil every drop," Muriel recalled. "It seemed a great adventure at the time, but when I saw Tigh na Brahan again today, I'm not sure I'd think the same way now."

She decided not to tell Mrs MacLeod she'd been caught trespassing, much less caught in a man's makeshift bedroom.

"So you met him, then?" Mrs MacLeod's sharp eyes caught the flush of colour on her guest's face. "They say Dominic Shaw's a mite touchy and keeps himself to himself. I dare say he's all right when you get to know him."

"Do they say how he's going to manage through the winter with no door or windows?" Muriel asked, taking the lead from her hostess's impersonal way of passing on information.

"They don't!" She laughed.

AFTER supper, Muriel walked down to the harbour to watch the fishing boats unload their catches. Ice cascaded down a chute from the great ice-plant, covering the fish-filled boxes. The loaders swiftly inserted hooks into handles at each end of the box and swung every box on to waiting trailers.

The pier was slippery with fish scales and melting ice, there were hoses and thick hawsers snaking from boat to shore, and great trucks preparing to drive away the loaded trailers. Above all was the greedy scream of gulls.

When Muriel and Robin had been to the pier with their father, everything was less highly mechanised. The men had time to stand and chat, sometimes they even gave Muriel's father a few small fish for their supper, while Robin collected small crabs caught up in the nets and not large enough to send to the markets.

"Stand back, lassie. You'll get a shower of ice down your neck." A big man in an orange apron and huge wellington boots gestured towards the ice chute which had changed direction to service another line of boxes. She stepped back quickly as the ice rattled down.

Suddenly she felt herself lifted up and swung round by strong arms.

"In trouble again, I see." The young man with dark hair put her down away from the moving hawser which she hadn't seen. She shook herself free as soon as she recognised the voice.

But as she stepped back another hawser caught her at the back of the knee and he took hold of her arm with a vice-like grip.

"What did I tell you?" There was amusement in his voice. "If I'd left you to your fate, it would have served you right."

Breathless, she struggled to regain her balance.

Before she could speak, the man let go and bowed.

"Shall we call a truce? I apologise if I was rude this afternoon, but you did break into my house uninvited. I should have picked you up then and thrown you out without a word. Let me introduce myself. Dominic Shaw."

He really was insufferable! Muriel looked at him and grinned.

"I do believe you have a sense of humour." Dominic laughed. "Then all is not lost."

Muriel told him her name and that she was staying with Mrs MacLeod. He took her elbow and guided her back from the pier.

"Let's get away from all this dangerous activity before you fall into the harbour." She didn't resist. In fact, she found his closeness strangely exciting.

"I didn't exactly 'break in' to Tigh na Brahan," she protested. "In fact, I'd no idea it belonged to anyone. I used to spend holidays there when I was small, and it had a kind of magic for me. It's a mistake, though, to return to favourite childhood places. They change, as we do . . ." And not always for the better, she thought.

They walked slowly along the sea wall and paused to look back at the bustling quay. The sun was low over the bay, a distant cluster of islands only crouching silhouettes.

Muriel became aware that he was watching her and felt the colour flood her face. She bit back the remark she'd been about to make, afraid he would mock her mood.

But his voice had softened.

"People and places don't change in the same way," he told her. "Memories are always there. Once it was summer for you at Tigh na Brahan, and so it can always be — for you. Why don't you come and see it again tomorrow? If I invite you, we can begin again and you'll probably find all the memories return — if you want them to . . ."

"I think I do. Thank you. I'd like to visit — and I promise I'll knock first."

S HE walked down the path again with a totally different feeling. For the first time since the beginning of this strange holiday she'd not thought of Murdo Forrester at all. Nor had she worried over the difficulties of leaving — if she left — Bailey's or about making up some convincing reason to give her parents.

She paused at the corner where the stream ran noisily over the rocks. Smoke rose lazily from the chimney of Tigh na Brahan and the faint acrid smell of peat reached her. Dominic was sawing wood and she could hear him whistling.

Return To Childhood Dreams

She was puzzled about her reaction to Dominic Shaw. Why did she feel this ache at the sight of him? Why resent so strongly his sharp teasing?

He'd only invited her to revisit childhood haunts and hadn't made any mention of accompanying her. She wondered if the cave, where she and Robin had been wicked pirates, was still there or was now silted full of sand. It looked as though it would soon be low tide so she could cross over the rocks to the little bay surrounded by cliffs where she and Robin were nearly cut off once as the tide turned.

The rock where her father used to catch mackerel in the deep part below the cliffs, the edge where her mother stretched out to sunbathe on the few warm days the Highlands boasted during the three weeks of their holiday. She must look for them, too.

Dominic was so busy sawing and measuring, planing pieces of wood and fitting one length into another that he didn't notice Muriel's

▶ *over*

GREAT BRITON

FLORENCE NIGHTINGALE

Although her parents were British, hospital reformer Florence Nightingale was born in Florence, Italy in 1820. While nursing in the Crimean War, she noted that most deaths did not occur from wounds but from insanitary hospital conditions. Thus she devoted her life to improving hospitals and their health arrangements. She set up colleges for training nurses in London hospitals, paving the way for nursing as we know it today.

Florence

approach. His dark hair was short, but thick curls fell forward over his face. A sleeveless white vest contrasted with his tanned skin. She stood and watched him for several minutes, smiling to herself.

"Is that the front door you're making?"

Dominic hammered his thumb and shouted an oath.

"I might have guessed," he said, nursing the bruised thumb beneath his arm. "Muriel James, you have a way of breaking into my thoughts and destroying not only my peace of mind but also my thumb . . ."

He sat down on the ground against the front wall of the cottage and motioned her to do likewise.

"Tell me what the cottage was like when you came here each summer," he suggested.

She began to describe the rooms, then went on to tell him about the cave, and the rock where her father caught mackerel. Then she told him about her father's illness and that she desperately needed to change her job.

"When I came away I hadn't made up my mind, but now I have," she said. "Suddenly, just now, I saw it quite clearly. I don't know why I thought the decision was difficult. It shouldn't be too hard to get another job as a computer operator these days." She felt suddenly light hearted.

"You get on with your front door." She laughed. "I'll go and look for the cave, indulge a few memories . . ."

Everything was there, just as she remembered it. She stood inside the cave and looked out, almost able to believe that Robin would leap off a ledge above her with blood-curdling yells, waving his spade in place of the cutlass it was meant to be.

The tide wasn't low enough to go round the rocks into the little bay after all. She'd no desire to be cut off and didn't intend to give Dominic any further cause to come to her rescue.

A S she made her way back along the beach and turned towards the cottage, Dominic emerged with two mugs of steaming tea.

"You'll never believe that this is the best drink for a warm day," he said. "Sugar?"

They sipped tea in comfortable companionship gazing out to sea. A laden coaster, low in the water, was barely moving halfway to the horizon.

"Tell me about the book," Muriel said. "I wouldn't know how to begin to write one."

"I've written it," Dominic replied. "The publishers have accepted it on condition I make some changes, do some re-writing of a couple of chapters." He looked at her as though weighing up whether he should confide in her. "I think — well, I'm pretty sure — it'll be a best-seller. The publisher was enthusiastic, you see, so I *must* get it right. I have to be somewhere quiet to work, somewhere that I can concentrate, without interruptions . . ." He sighed. "Then you walked into Tigh na Brahan —"

"If you feel like that," Muriel began, "I'll go, don't bother to throw me out." She put down her mug and began to get to her feet.

"Oh, Muriel, Muriel . . ."

When Dominic put his arms round her, the sudden anger evaporated. He held her close and this time she didn't want to resist.

"You've been so badly hurt," he whispered. Not a question. A statement. To say he understood.

She was afraid she was going to cry. She blinked and dared the tears to run down her face. The sun glistened very brightly on the sea.

Gradually she felt her body relax. She felt safe. Her head felt comfortable against his shoulder.

"Of course you mustn't go," he whispered, his lips against her hair. "I can imagine you being here always."

☆   ☆   ☆   ☆

"It's a shame your home's so far away," Mrs MacLeod said after supper that evening. "With your experience, you'd be just what the manager at the Ach-na-Mara Hotel is looking for. They say he's installed a computer and now can't find anyone who knows how to work it."

She chattered on about what one of the hotel waitresses had told her. There'd been an argument with the receptionist, it seems, but Muriel was hardly listening. The whole idea was quite fantastic. But possible. It was almost as if opportunity was battering at her door.

"Do they say how many applicants there are for the job?" she asked Mrs MacLeod, feeling quite light headed at the possibility of a future plan which would solve all her problems with one all-embracing sweep.

"Not one," the older woman replied with a laugh. "You see, there's no-one around here trained for that sort of thing." She looked closely at Muriel. "You're not . . . are you? I believe you are . . My, my! Now, wouldn't that be just great? Will you be going round to see the manager in the morning?"

☆   ☆   ☆   ☆

Muriel is now head receptionist at the Ach-na-Mara Hotel and is teaching the other girls how to use the computer. Dominic's book is due to appear next month and the film rights have already been sold. Tigh na Brahan is finished and there are chintz curtains again at the windows. The front door has no forbidding notice attached to it but stands open whenever the sun shines.

For Muriel, memory and reality have come closer together. Once, it was summer in her memory of Tigh na Brahan. Now, all the seasons are just as precious. She and Dominic were married when the book was published, and he's more than halfway through the sequel.

For Muriel Shaw has watched her father slowly regain hesitant speech as he sat and watched the summer sea. Her mother sunbathed on the rock above the beach. And brother Robin has threatened to visit next year with his new and pretty Chinese wife when they come on leave from Hong Kong.

For Muriel, Tigh na Brahan will have come full circle. □

The Price Of Progress

MORNA picked up the official-looking envelope and her heart did a sudden leap. For a moment she found it hard to breathe and she rested against the wall of the passage.

She couldn't go back into the dining-room until she felt calmer. She didn't even want to show Walter the letter, just yet. Walter would know what it was, just as she did, and she didn't think she could stand his sympathy just now. And not only sympathy.

Walter would explain, as he had been doing for the past weeks, that they had known sooner or later Bray Cottage would be torn down. But

by
PHIL
MANSTON

that didn't make it any easier to lose the home you had loved for all your married life.

Just because the "powers-that-be" had decided the new motorway must go where the three cottages now stood, didn't make it right, or easier to bear.

Angrily, Morna pushed the letter, unopened, into her pocket and returned to her seat at the breakfast table.

However, once Walter had left for work, she opened the envelope and read the words which spoke of a compulsory order and told her they had the right of appeal. Tears filled her eyes until she couldn't see the words.

"How very kind," she told the empty room scathingly. "They buy my home without so much as a by-your-leave and then say we have the right to argue. Fat lot of good that will do us, I know."

But, even as she said the words, Morna felt something rising inside her. Rebellion was the only word for it.

When it had all been only hearsay and rumour there had been nothing concrete to fight, but now, with those monstrous words staring up at her, she found her resolve hardening.

This was *her* home. It was where their children had grown up. Lisa and Jed had toddled round the garden, run down the lane on their way to and from school, given and received first kisses under the shadow of the old oak tree.

Lisa and Jed had their own homes now. Spanking new semis with all the modern gadgets, but Morna couldn't imagine herself in such a place. The raw, red bricks, the trim gardens and the coldly hygienic kitchens didn't seem like a home to her eyes.

She swallowed hard. This was no time for sentiment. Sentiment would have no effect on officialdom. She needed logic; cold, reasoned, arguments.

CLEARING the breakfast dishes, she tried to think of something she could put forward in an appeal. She tried to remember everything she had heard about other such cases, but nothing seemed to apply to Bray Cottage.

There must be something, she thought, looking out through the bedroom window later, imagining the roar of cars along the road which was to take the place of the quiet country lane. In her mind she could hear the screech of brakes, and a shudder ran through her.

Someone had to make a stand. Perhaps the occupants of the other cottages would back her up? Old Mr Grant from Corner Cottage, would he fight?

No, maybe not. Corner Cottage was in poor repair, with not even the basic modern amenities. The old man would be glad to move into a flat where everything came at the press of a switch.

Mr and Mrs Hyde then? They had bought the cottage as a country retreat after their busy days in city offices. Surely they would want to preserve their little haven?

But, once more Morna had to admit defeat. The Hydes were

spending less and less time in the village. She had heard a rumour that they now owned a villa in Spain.

Morna smoothed out the crumpled letter, examining the sketch map intently, tracing the line of the proposed road which ran right through the three cottages. Could it be built somewhere else, take a slightly different route?

But though she peered relentlessly, comparing the sketch with an Ordnance Survey map, she had to admit there seemed no other way. It was clear that they couldn't pull down the whole estate of new houses which lay beyond the field, just to save the cottages.

B UT why my living-room?" she questioned Walter, when he came home that evening and she was forced to show him the letter.

"It's tough, I know, love. But it's the price of progress," Walter told her.

"Progress!" Morna snorted. "It's bureaucracy gone mad. That's what it is."

"Not really. We're not the first and we'll not be the last. I can't see what we can do about it. Not unless . . ." His eyes twinkled. "Not unless you feel like staging a sit-in.

"They're already at Markham," he said, his voice sobering as he spoke of the nearby market town. "And the red markers are flying across Willie Stell's fields."

Walter caught the exasperated look Morna threw at him and decided to change the subject. She'd get used to the idea in time. She'd have to.

But she didn't intend getting used to anything of the sort. Walter had spoken of a sit-in with amusement, but the thought lodged in her mind. It would, at least, make these officials sit up and take notice, she thought. And maybe she'd win a bit of sympathy.

Morna's vivid imagination pictured the newspaper accounts, TV coverage, maybe. And she began to make her plans.

One Saturday Morna looked out of the bedroom window to see the bulldozers grouped at the end of the lane. Monday, she knew, was the

GREAT BRITON

KATHLEEN FERRIER

One of Britain's best-loved singers, Kathleen Ferrier was a native of Higher Walton, Lancashire. By the age of sixteen she had earned a certificate as a piano teacher, but it wasn't until 1940, at the age of twenty-eight, that she attained singing success. Giving up her job as a telephone operator, she began to study voice and gave recitals to factory workers. Kathleen went on to become an oratorio singer of highest rank, performing in top operas. She died of cancer in 1953, in the prime of her singing career.

deadline. They had a few days grace while the workmen prepared the way and assessed the problem and she guessed that Bray Cottage would be the last house to be tackled.

They had been offered a flat in a three-storey block on the edge of Markham.

"It's not a bad place," Morna had allowed, when they'd gone to inspect it. And she'd seen the way Walter's face had brightened.

Autumn Leaves

THE old leaves come rustling
  Hustling and bustling,
Hurrying, scurrying over the lawn,
Brown leaves and red leaves
Yellow and dead leaves
Whispering sadly that summer has flown.

How madly they're twirling,
Skirling and swirling,
Dancing and prancing into a heap.
Wild winds are dashing them
Winter rain lashing them,
Whilst all around them the trees are
  asleep.

Blackbirds will scatter them,
Underfoot shatter them
Searching for insects that burrow
  beneath.
Snowflakes will cover them
Softly lie over them
As they merge thankfully into the heath.

Spring-time will come again
Then trees will bloom again
Bursting their buds with a vigour reborn.
Woods will be green again
Then will be seen again
Lovely young leaves on the trees they
  adorn.

— *T. McCann.*

"Then you'll take it, love? It is nice and central, yet it's not too far from the country."

He knew how Morna loved the countryside with its flowers and fields. Leaving her garden would be a wrench, but he had some ideas how to mimimise her loss.

"Country!" Morna had sniffed. A view of distant hills and a few stunted trees scattered along the edge of a couple of scrubby fields wasn't what she called country.

Walter had taken the keys of the flat and he had spent most evenings there, painting the rooms and putting up extra cupboards in the tiny kitchen; Morna had a thing about storage space.

When the great machines were moved into the garden of Corner Cottage Walter brought Morna a cup of tea in bed.

"The removal men are booked for Wednesday. Will you be ready, love?" he asked tentatively.

"Yes, I'll be ready," she said, sipping her tea thoughtfully.

All that day she worked methodically, packing bedding and crockery, and all the other things they could manage without for a day or two. Walter viewed the full packing cases with satisfaction.

Morna had accepted the inevitable, he thought. In fact, judging by the heightened colour in her cheeks and the sparkle in her eyes, she might even be feeling excited at the prospect. Whistling, he set about the task of lifting the carpets and rolling them ready for the removal men.

WEDNESDAY was the sort of day people pray to have when they're moving house — bright, crisp, without a sign of rain.

Walter had taken the day off. He was only working his time out now, so he wouldn't be missed very much. He quite enjoyed helping the two sturdy young men to load the van.

At last the house was almost empty and as the men fastened the large van doors, Walter went to look for Morna. He thought she'd be having a last nostalgic look round and moved quietly. But, when at first he couldn't see her, he began to call her name as he mounted the stairs.

"Morna! Morna, love. Are you ready? The men are leaving now. They're going for their lunch on the way, but you'll want to get to the flat before them, I expect."

Morna's face popped round the door of what had been Jed's room until his marriage some years before.

"You get into the car, Walter."

Nodding automatically Walter turned to go back downstairs. Then he hesitated.

"What about you? Aren't you coming yet?"

She shook her head, teardrops falling from her lashes.

"No. I can't come, Walter, not yet." She saw he didn't understand. "You suggested a sit-in, so that's what I'm going to do.

"I'm only taking a leaf out of other people's books." She put up a hand as he started to protest. "It's the done thing nowadays, isn't it?"

"But, Morna!" Walter gasped. "You can't mean it."

"Yes, I do." The door started to close between them. "You get along. This is my protest. I'll be all right."

"But, Morna, you can't! I mean . . ." Walter was lost for words.

"It's only a house," he said at last. "Somewhere to live. Four walls and a roof. I mean, all this . . ." He spread his hands in helpless fashion.

Morna stared at him in amazement. Was that all Bray Cottage meant to him? All these years together, all their lives?

"This is *our* home. We came here when we were first married." Her voice broke as she tried to explain how she felt. "Our children grew up here. I know every nook and cranny of the place, all filled with memories."

"I know, Morna. Believe me, I do know. I do understand how you feel."

Walter gazed about him.

"Why, isn't this the very floorboard Jed tripped over that time when I'd got the carpet up for something or other? Do you recall what a gash he got? He's got the scar to this day.

"And here's where I spilt that can of paint when I was painting the cot for little Lisa." He chuckled.

Walter didn't look at his wife, but walked slowly towards the back bedroom.

"See, you can still see the scratches Jed made when he tried to prise up some boards looking for buried treasure. I didn't half wallop him for that escapade. Remember?"

He looked reflectively at the palm of his hand as if the imprint of that punishment might show there. And he heard Morna chuckle.

"Yes," she said. "I thought you'd kill him that day. So, Walter, you do remember?"

"Yes, lass. I remember." Walter put out a hand and took hers gently. "Come along, my dear. Like I said, the old place is only made of bricks and mortar, but I don't think it would approve of what you're planning. It seems a bit undignified, don't you think? It's been a good place, a good home, but it's had its day. Let it rest, love."

Morna looked at him for a long moment.

"Maybe you're right," she said finally. "I hadn't thought of that."

Her eyes went sadly round the room but she allowed him to lead her down to the waiting car.

The drive to the block of flats was swift but silent and Walter saw how Morna stared resolutely through the window, yet he knew she wasn't seeing the streets they passed through.

GREAT BRITON

J. M. BARRIE

Kirriemuir, a small textile town in Tayside, was the birthplace of the famous author James Matthew Barrie. Of his novels and plays, he is best remembered for the classic children's fantasy, "Peter Pan." Today, his house is owned by the National Trust and is open to visitors. The building which inspired Barrie's Wendy house still stands and visitors to the town can see the places he wrote about in some of his works.

Kirriemuir

GOING up in the lift, the shiny, new key in his fingers, Walter hoped Morna would like the surprise he'd planned for her.

The key turned easily in the lock and Walter stepped back to allow his wife to go in first. Morna stood on the threshold, her eyes flashing round the cold, impersonal hallway. Then she gave a little surprised gasp.

On the wall, where she couldn't help seeing it each time she came into the flat, hung a picture of Bray Cottage. And clustered around it were miniature paintings of some of the many blooms she had planted and nurtured in their garden.

"Oh, Walter," she breathed, turning into his arms. "They're lovely. And it's just like you to be so thoughtful. I thought I was supposed to be the sentimental one."

Walter kissed her gently, laughing down into her face.

"You weren't being so sentimental back there, talking of a sit-in. Woman of action, that was you."

He eyed his wife speculatively as she walked round the small, cluttered sitting-room

"Everything is all right now, isn't it? You aren't unhappy? You've resigned yourself?"

"The flat's fine." Morna nodded then shook her head, the corners of her mouth lifting. "Especially with the improvements you've made, my dear."

She came to stand before him, lifting her hand, almost as if about to ruffle his hair as she'd done to Jed when he was small. But instead she laid it against his cheek tenderly.

"Don't worry, I know we'll be happy here. How could I help with you along? But . . . resigned? Oh, no! In fact . . ."

Morna's eyes went to the packing cases.

"As soon as I've unpacked that lot and put them away, I'm going to write a letter."

"A letter, love?"

"Mmm! Well, an application, actually. To join an action group I read about. This time the bureaucrats have won, but another time? Ah! Now there's no telling what might happen another time, is there?" She grinned, her eyes shining with excitement. □

The Change

by PHYLLIS HEATH

D IANE MATHER turned eagerly from the cooker as she heard her
husband's key in the lock. "Oh, Les, I'm so glad you're early,"
she called, running to meet him. "Don't take your things off, I
want you to do an errand for me, please," she wheedled, seeing the look
on his face. "It's for Patricia. I need a bobbin of thread, to match this,"
Diane said, offering Les a scrap of bright material.

Les simply stood there, eyeing the material but making no move
towards the door. Then after a moment he began to unzip his jacket.

In Patricia

"Les?" Diane's voice faltered. "Didn't you understand? I asked you to slip along to the corner shop. Mrs Law will have what I need, I'm sure."

"I heard you," Les said, but continued to take off his jacket. "Look, it's pouring out there. I'm tired and wet. I don't want to go out again. You can get the cotton tomorrow."

Diane laughed, a little unsure, putting a finger on her young husband's forehead to smooth away the wrinkles. "Now don't be an old grumps. Tomorrow won't do. I need the thread to finish Patricia's party dress. Don't tease me. I know that's what you're doing, but your dinner's all ready and it will spoil, and there's no sense in me going when you're wet already, is there?"

She held out the wet jacket. "Come on, love, don't be silly."

"Silly? Who's silly? Certainly not me. Patricia's got lots of dresses. And I'm not going out again. And that's final!" he shouted, dashing the garment from Diane's fingers.

It lay on the floor between them, a wet, blue puddle, and Diane stared at it in amazement. "Les? Les, what's got into you?"

He had begun to move away, but at her words he swung round. "I'll tell you what's got into me — a bit of sense. You make that child into a god. The whole house, your whole world, revolves around her — and she's only four. What will you be like when she's fourteen?"

Diane stared at him, unable to believe her ears, or what her brain was telling her. "You're jealous! Jealous of your own daughter. Les Mather, how could you?"

Tears filled her eyes but she brushed them away angrily. She'd suspected that Les wasn't over fond of their child, but this?

"I've never put her before you. Any other father would be pleased that his daughter was pretty and that I did everything I could to make her look even nicer. I can't understand you."

"Diane." Les reached for her but she stepped away, watching him warily. "I'm not jealous, believe me it's not that. Yes, Patricia is lovely and you look after her so well. But . . . oh, I can't explain. There's something . . ." His words tailed away but Diane wasn't really listening as she began to pull on her coat.

"Don't bother to try," she cried. "I'll get the cotton myself. At least *I* care that our child should be happy."

DIANE tore out of the house, not waiting to see if Les would call her back but, as she reached the path, she heard him on the step behind her, and thinking he was going to offer to do the errand she turned on him.

"Don't bother! I know you never want to do anything with Patricia. You never even play with her like a normal father would."

She saw Les's face go white but she was past caring and when he started to speak she scarcely listened.

"Shall I tell you why? Because I'm a grown man, Diane. I can't play with a doll. Dolls are for little girls," he snarled, shutting the door with a slam.

Diane hesitated a moment but then dismissed his words. What kind of thing was that to say, she thought, as she began to run down the path. But, all at once, her feet shot from under her and the breath was knocked from her body as she hit the ground, pain shooting from where her hip had made contact with the hard paving stones.

She tried to call for Les but the pain was so intense she felt her head swimming and the next thing she knew she was feeling herself being lifted on to the settee back in the house. Les and another man were bending over her.

"I'll phone for an ambulance," the stranger said. "It's a good thing I happened to be passing."

Les nodded, kneeling down by his wife and holding her hands between his.

"You'll be all right, love. Don't worry. We'll get you to hospital where they can give you a good examination. I think you've broken your leg," he told her gently, all sign of his previous anger gone.

The next hour passed in a blur of pain for Diane until, at last, she was stretched out in a narrow hospital bed, feeling delightfully drowsy as the pain ebbed away.

"I'll be back," Les whispered. "You're to sleep now."

The Race

WE ran a good race did Dickie and me,
Along by the beach and then down to the sea.
Lemmy, the Labrador, joined in, too,
And so did Amanda and curly-haired Sue.

They are the girls who are staying next door.
They're nice, but we thought that their running was poor,
So we gave them a start when we all raced back,
As far as the man in the bright yellow mac.

But Dickie fell down, then I lost a shoe,
And then we just didn't know what we could do,
For the girls ran on swiftly before we'd begun.
Poor running, indeed! Do you know? They won!

— *Valerie Appleby.*

He bent to kiss her and for a few seconds Diane surfaced as his words got through to her.

"Les, Les," she whispered, her mouth feeling strange so that she had difficulty forming the words. "Patricia? What about Patricia?"

"Don't worry, everything's been taken care of. You just get to sleep, now."

Diane nodded, though at what she wasn't sure. But later, when the drug had worn off and she was lying awake in the crowded ward, she began to worry, despite Les's words. Both their parents lived some distance off and it wouldn't be easy for either set to come down here.

Perhaps it won't be for long, Diane thought. Maybe Les will take some time off work and then, when they put a proper plaster on, I'll be able to hobble about. I'll manage then, she consoled herself.

HOWEVER, that wasn't to be the case. The doctor came and told her she would have to stay for some days. When she protested that her little girl needed her, he patted her hand. "Now don't you fret about anything. I'm sure your husband will make some arrangements. All you have to do is rest, do as the nurses say, and get better as quickly as possible. Someone else will be wanting this bed before very long, so we want you out of here as much as you want to leave."

He smiled but Diane could scarcely smile back and she waited anxiously for Les's appearance that evening.

"How's Patricia?" she asked, the moment he appeared.

He didn't seem to want to meet her eyes. "Er . . . well, she's fine. Just fine! I'll have to go back to work, you know," he went on and Diane felt alarm gathering inside her.

"Les, where's Patricia? What have you done?"

"Heavens, Diane! What do you imagine I've done with the child? She's being looked after."

"Looked after?" Diane's voice squeaked. "How do you mean?"

"She . . . I had to do something," Les stumbled. "But she's fine, I tell you. She's with Mrs Talbot. She's a foster mother. She takes children like Patricia . . . you know, when their mothers are sick, or something. Takes them into her home and cares for them, along with her own children. She's very nice."

"Nice! You've left our child with a woman you don't know? Are you mad?"

"No, just desperate. But Tricia is happy, love. I go and see her, and she's . . ."

"Fine," Diane supplied, caustically. "So you keep saying."

"But she is. She was running about with the Talbot kids, laughing and playing. As happy as a sandboy. You don't have to worry, love. She didn't even . . . she doesn't seem to have . . ."

His face flushed bright red and Diane guessed what he'd nearly said. Patricia hadn't asked after her mother, she wasn't fretting.

Diane bit her lip, trying to be happy that the child wasn't sad and worrying, but she couldn't help feeling a little hurt that she wasn't even being missed. She covered her face, knowing the jealousy she was feeling towards this unknown woman must show there. And *she'd* accused Les of being jealous.

LATER that night, when she couldn't sleep, Diane thought about her feelings, and the way she'd treated her husband. Could she have been neglecting him? If she felt jealous of a stranger, perhaps Les

95

could have been jealous of her attention to Patricia and all with some cause.

But Patricia's a child, she told herself. She needs my love and attention. And more so, since her father scarcely seems to know she's around. He's never paid her much attention. Never!

Yet Les had wanted the baby, just as much as she had. Why was he so different now?

Her mind went back to the days of her pregnancy. They'd been so close then, planning and preparing for their baby. Les had decorated the little room, even though Diane had laughed at him, saying the baby would be too little to be alone right at first.

"But he'll grow." Les had laughed.

"Hey! He might be a girl. What then?" She had smiled as she asked the question, half believing that Les might be upset if the baby wasn't a boy. But he had hugged her to him, kissing her ears and the tip of her nose — his special way of telling her he loved her.

"I want a baby. Your baby, my baby, I don't care what it is."

"Sometimes," she said ruefully, touching her swollen stomach," I think it's a hippo. But I'll settle for a boy or a girl."

They'd laughed together and she'd gone back to her knitting whilst he went on painting the cot.

He'd been so struck with wonder when the tiny infant was put into his arms that Diane's heart had come up into her throat and she felt she'd never loved anyone quite so much. But he did seem a little frightened, too, sure he would break Patricia with his large workman's hands.

"You'll get over that," Diane assured him. "When we're home and she's got a bit chubbier. Babies don't break easily," she told him with new-found knowledge.

Yet, as the months passed he persisted in viewing the growing child with a mixture of awe and fear which Diane began to find irritating. Though, by the time Patricia was one, she had grown used to his attitude and seldom asked him to do anything for his daughter.

Patricia thrived without her father's attention. Diane had been thrilled to see what a bonnie baby she'd managed to produce. She was under no illusions about her own plainness and had, in fact, often wondered what Les had seen in her. He was quite handsome himself, tall and fair with twinkling eyes and a ready smile. Diane knew that all her friends had envied her when they had got engaged.

She wished as the time of the birth drew near that the child would take after its father, and was overjoyed when she recognised his long eyelashes, deep-blue eyes and blonde curls. If Les was good looking, how much lovelier would a girl be with these attributes?

B UT behind all her pleasure lurked that one sadness, the fact that Les didn't seem to want to be close to his daughter, didn't want to love and play with her. Was that why he hadn't seemed to care that some stranger was now taking care of their daughter?

Tears overflowed on to Diane's pillow and a passing nurse turned to speak to her.

The Change In Patricia

"Now, now, we can't have this, my dear. What's the matter? Of course! It's your little girl, isn't it? You must miss her. And you're no doubt worrying about her, too? Yes, I thought so," she added as Diane nodded.

"Now, you promise to go straight to sleep and stop worrying and I'll ask Sister about letting her pay you a visit. How's that?"

Diane's face broke into a huge smile. "Oh, I'll sleep for a week if only I can see Patricia."

"Well, there wouldn't be much point in her coming if you're going to be asleep," the young woman teased. "But we'll see what we can do."

Diane could scarcely wait for the visiting time the day the Sister had said Mrs Talbot was bringing Patricia to see her. She sat watching the doors to the hall as the hour drew near, her eyes and ears straining for the first sign of them.

When she heard an excited voice in the hall and the clip-clip of tiny shoes she leaned forward, as if by doing so Patricia would be with her all the sooner. But, as she listened to the firm footsteps of a woman and the tripping ones of a child, Diane felt uneasy. Something was wrong. Something she couldn't put her finger on, but which worried her.

Then into the ward stepped a little girl holding tightly to the hand of a middle-aged woman. Instinct told her this was Patricia and, certainly, nothing could disguise her golden curls or the large, bright blue eyes gleaming in her face. But this wasn't the child she'd left behind.

As the pair drew nearer Diane realised what had been different about

GREAT BRITON

FLORA MACDONALD

Born in 1722 in Milton, South Uist, Flora Macdonald was the Jacobite supporter who helped Bonnie Prince Charlie to escape from Benbecula after his defeat at the battle of Culloden in 1746. Flora was betrayed by a boatman, and was sent to prison in London.

On her release she returned to Scotland, where she later married. In 1774 she and her family emigrated to America, where her husband was appointed brigadier-general in the Civil War. When he was captured and imprisoned Flora returned to Scotland, her husband returning some time later. Flora died in 1790.

South Uist

G

their approach down the hall. Gone were the dainty white slippers Patricia normally wore. Poking out from under the hems of a tiny pair of blue jeans were two bright red clogs!

Diane swallowed, shaking her head as if she couldn't believe what she was seeing. Clogs and jeans! On Patricia! Where were her own clothes?

Yorkshire's Magic

THE lanes wind on for ever,
  They never seem to end,
There is always something beautiful
  Around every single bend.

Dark hawthorns in the background,
  The blackbird starts to sing,
The golden sheen of daffodils
  Reminds us here is spring.

June brings out wild roses,
  The landscape casts its spell,
The moors and rugged hillsides,
  The foxgloves in the dell.

Summer fades to autumn,
  The moors turn brown and gold,
Casting lovely shadows
  As the days grow dull and cold.

Winter spreads her icy grip,
  Streams are frozen bare,
The meadows all arrayed in white
  The bracing, frosty air.

Away from cares of city life,
  Here is Yorkshire's wonderland.
Each season holds a magic
  Man will never understand.
      — E. Saddington.

Numbly she shook hands with Mrs Talbot whilst a suddenly shy Patricia tried to hide behind the woman's skirts, peeping from under the hood of a bright red anorak. Where was her own beautiful, fur-trimmed, blue coat?

"Come on, love." Mrs Talbot swung the child up on to the bed beside her mother, and at last Patricia looked at her, her eyes round and solemn.

"Hello, Patricia," Diane said softly, recognising the strangeness of the hospital in the little girl's eyes. She longed to gather her into her arms, but she held back.

"H'lo," Patricia said at last. "Why you in bed? It's not bedtime."

"Mummy's been poorly, pet," Mrs Talbot said. "Remember, I told you."

Patricia nodded. "Mummy poorly." Her voice rose enquiringly. "Mummy?" she questioned, testing the word. "Mummy!" she squealed and flung herself into Diane's arms.

DIANE hugged her, the two of them laughing, both not far from tears.

"Phew!" Mrs Talbot sighed with relief. "The first part's always a bit tricky."

Diane ignored her, holding Patricia and whispering her name over and over.

For a little while Patricia allowed her mother to hold her, but then she pushed herself away, sitting back and looking at Diane sternly.

"Me Trixie," she announced with a touch of resolution.

Diane looked from the small determined face to the woman beside the bed and saw the embarrassed colour running up into Mrs Talbot's cheeks.

"I'm sorry about that, Mrs Mather," she said. "It's the other children. I've got two at the moment as well as your daughter. Jeffrey's only two and he can't say Patricia."

Diane didn't speak. What could she say? This woman hadn't had her child five minutes, it seemed, yet already she wasn't the same child. Mrs Talbot noticed Diane's fingers on the child's anorak. "Her other things . . . well, they're so beautiful I was afraid they'd get spoiled. The boys are a bit rough when they play, you see."

Diane shuddered but before she could speak, Patricia was sliding to the floor.

"Trixie got clogs. See! They go clonk, clonk." She chortled and proceeded to demonstrate, running up and down the ward.

When at last she clambered back on to the bed her eyes were gleaming with mischief, her cheeks rosy with exertion. Just at that moment Les pushed open the doors.

"Daddy! Daddy," Patricia screamed and she was off again, throwing herself against his legs.

Les swung her up into his arms. "Hush! No noise here. I told you."

"Yes, Daddy," Patricia whispered obediently as he sat down with her. She wriggled until she was curled on his lap, legs jutting foward. "You like my clogs?"

Les's gaze went from the clogs to Mrs Talbot and then to Diane, and his wife saw the worried frown which gathered on his brow.

She looked at the red clogs and at her daughter's face and then up into Les's eyes. What was it he had shouted after her just before she fell? "I can't play with dolls." Was that what she'd given him? Not a living, breathing, loving child but a dressed-up dummy, a doll?

No wonder he'd been scared of her. No wonder he'd thought she might break. It wasn't the child he was afraid of hurting but the clothes which she had spent hours slaving over. He did love her. He simply hadn't been able to get close enough to show his love.

Diane looked towards Mrs Talbot and she smiled. "Thank you for looking after my little girl. I can see you've made her very happy."

She felt Les move to sit on the bed close to her and put a hand out to him. "But all the same I'm going to get well just as quickly as I can," she told them. "I want to come home. Home to him and . . . and Trixie."

She felt Les's arm come round her and, despite the presence of Mrs Talbot and the other patients, they kissed lovingly.

As she lay close in his arms Patricia burrowed to get closer, too. "Make room for me," she yelled, as Les and Diane opened their arms to draw her to them.

"Yes, hurry home, Diane," Les whispered. "We've got to get started on being a proper family, don't you agree?"

There was no doubt that Diane and Patricia did. □

MISS RITCHIE lived in one of the very finest flats in the west end of town. Her first name was Wilma though no-one had used it since she was in her teens.

When she finished at university and joined the Civil Service she was immediately known as Miss Ritchie. There was a time during her advancement in the Board of Trade when she was known as Miss R., but it was soon back to Miss Ritchie again.

Late in her career she was awarded the OBE for her distinguished service to the nation. There had been a few letters of congratulation, one or two handshakes, but no celebration parties.

She accepted her honour as a natural consequence of her hard work and devotion to her job and simply got on with it.

When, in due course, her retirement came along she accepted the inevitability of that too. She shook a few hands and walked back to her beautifully-furnished flat, made herself a cup of tea and sat down to review her life.

Not entirely to her surprise, she reached the conclusion that in one aspect she had been a failure. Financially, of course, she had done better than she had imagined, even in her wildest dreams, and she smiled a little as she remembered the tiny house she had been born into sixty years earlier. Quite a difference from her modern, luxury flat.

And that, she told herself ruefully, was really all she had. Apart from enjoying the solitude of listening to Chopin or Brahms, or reading a historical biography, she'd never had a hobby through which she might have met other people with similar interests.

MISS RITCHIE'S LAST WISH

by SANDY REID

She allowed herself a slight smile as she remembered that she had never made a friend.

Certainly there had been an occasion, while visiting the Colosseum during a holiday in Rome, she had become friendly with an Oxford professor of English.

He had been keen to advance their friendship, but she had refused. Her career had been everything to her — and nothing, but nothing, was allowed to interfere with that.

So Miss Ritchie settled down to a comfortable, but totally uneventful, retirement. She only spoke when absolutely necessary to neighbours and local shopkeepers, all of whom regarded her as a polite and civil recluse.

SO the months passed quietly until the day a shattering pain suddenly struck her. She slumped down on to the sofa until she could comfortably draw breath.

This wasn't the first time she had felt the pain, but never as bad as this before. And she decided, though she regarded it a great weakness on her part, to call her doctor.

Miss Ritchie had seldom required a doctor during her lifetime, but Dr Bone had looked after her from time to time, treating any minor illness she had had. After a brief examination and listening carefully to all Miss Ritchie said, he told her she would have to go into hospital for a further examination.

She went into a rather grand nursing home nearby, where she had an exploratory operation. After a few days she felt better and she was allowed home.

Dr Bone called on her at her flat a few days later and Miss Ritchie demanded to know exactly what was wrong with her.

Dr Bone started a long-winded explanation but Miss Ritchie interrupted him.

"I want a brief, accurate diagnosis," she said. "So please start again."

Dr Bone decided it would be futile to beat about the bush.

"I'm afraid you are a very sick woman, Miss Ritchie."

"And?" she prompted.

"You are going to die," he said, after a pause.

"That I know," said Miss Ritchie. "Aren't we all? The point is, when?"

"I can't tell you that exactly," he replied.

"But surely, if you were to hazard a guess, would it be days, weeks, months, years . . . ?"

"I would say a matter of months."

"Thank you," said Miss Ritchie, "and in the meantime am I supposed to lie here and calmly wait for eternal judgment?"

"Of course not," Dr Bone answered. "If you feel well enough to get up and get out and about, do so. You can do anything you feel like doing. Live your life to the full."

"Well, that's a comfort," she said. "Thank you for calling."

After the doctor had gone Miss Ritchie suddenly realised she didn't feel as brave as she had pretended to be and tears fell down cheeks which hadn't seen tears for many years.

WHEN she had eventually composed herself she thought back to her childhood. She thought of the humble, two-roomed tenement home, where she had been born.

Her thoughts moved on to the three-roomed council house, with the wonderful, first-ever bathroom, when her father had decided he could afford the rent. And finally the great day when, with the help of a mortgage, they had moved into a four-roomed, semi-detached bungalow.

She was twenty then and had just finished college and how she had enjoyed the luxury of sitting in the garden of her family's lovingly-maintained home.

They were happy days, she thought.

▶ *p104*

If Portmeirion doesn't look like a typical Welsh village but more like a Mediterranean town, there is a good reason for it — it was built in Southern Italian style by the architect Sir Clough Williams-Ellis. Portmeirion stand on a peninsula at the top of Tremadog Bay, and being privately owned, the village is only open to visitors in the summer months when one of its attractions is the shop which sells the well-known Portmeirion pottery.

Gordon Henderson

PORTMEIRION, GWYNEDD

The tenement house with the huge iron grate and oven. She remembered climbing on top of the oven and snuggling down in the warmth that glowed all around her.

The council house, where she had first enjoyed central heating and where her father had bought her her first bike. How nice it would be to see them all again, each producing memories of its different and distinctive brand of love, humour and affection — something she had forgotten existed during her successful years.

Woodland Stream

LITTLE woodland stream
   Sparkling in the sun,
Spilling forth your waters
   In simple, joyful fun.
Over mossy stones you chatter
   Your waters tumbling bright,
Reflecting darting sunbeams
   In the early morning light.
Where silver birches stand,
   Tall and straight and bold,

Between grassy lea and meadowland
   Carpeted in gold.
Beside grassy banks of clover,
   With bluebells in array,
You sing your song of welcome
   On this first springtime day.
Onward ever onward
   Till you reach the journey's end,
There to join the river
   Where your waters brightly blend.
          — *Charles B. Watkins.*

A week later, it was wonderful how well she still felt, and she decided to hire a chauffeur-driven car, so she could pay visits to all her old homes. The car came for her at ten o'clock the next morning and she gave the driver his instructions.

She sat back in the car quite happily. What fun, she thought. It was a daft idea, but she hadn't enjoyed herself so much in years.

About twenty minutes later they were parked beside the little bungalow which had been her last family home. Miss Ritchie slowly stepped out of the car.

AT first glance the house looked much the same as she had remembered it. Then she noticed the garden. The small lawn was tufty and unkempt, the roses had more briar than bush to them and the whole place was overgrown with weeds.

Miss Ritchie walked up to the front door and a middle-aged woman emerged.

"Forgive me," said Miss Ritchie. "I have no business to be here, but forty years ago I lived here and I just thought I would like to see the old place again."

"Well, fancy that," said Mrs Croft, who now owned the house. "Has it changed?"

"Not really," Miss Ritchie replied honestly.

Mrs Croft's eyes looked on her garden.

"I'm sure your garden was better cared for than it is now."

Miss Ritchie smiled and nodded at Mrs Croft sympathetically.

"Ah well," sighed Mrs Croft, "there would be a man about the house I expect."

"There was, my father was a very keen gardener."

"So was my husband," said Mrs Croft, "but he died a few years back and what with my arthritis and one thing or another I'm afraid the garden has suffered. Maybe some day I'll get round to paying a man to look after things. But gardeners cost the earth these days."

Miss Ritchie smilingly agreed, thanked Mrs Croft for sparing the time to talk to her and took her leave.

Back in the car she gave the driver another address and ten minutes later they stopped at a modest, well-cared-for council flat.

A middle-aged woman wearing an apron came to the door when Miss Ritchie rang the bell.

"I'm not buying anything today," she said, then she paused. "You look a bit old to be out selling anything," she added.

Miss Ritchie smiled.

"I can assure you I'm not selling anything," she said. "It's just that, oh, it must be forty-five years ago I lived in your house and I thought it would be nice to see the old place again."

"Oh dear," said Mrs Nelson, "I'd like to ask you to come in, but the house is a mess and I'm busy trying to lick it into some kind of shape. With four boys and a husband in the house it's hard to keep things as tidy as you'd like."

"It must indeed be difficult," agreed Miss Ritchie, "but you know it must have been more difficult when I lived here. We had no washing machines or spin dryers in those days."

"And I haven't got any such things now," said Mrs Nelson. "The eldest of my sons is fourteen and he's for ever asking for a bike, so a washing machine will have to wait for a while yet."

"You know, I remember getting my very first bike when I lived here. And a second-hand one it was, too. However, I expect you'll manage," she concluded. ▶ *p108*

THE HERMITAGE, DUNKELD *(see over)*

Just outside the lovely Perthshire town of Dunkeld, The Hermitage has been well known to visitors to the Highlands for over two hundred years. The then Duke of Atholl built the original "Hermitage" in these grounds but the present building, like a summer house and known as Ossian's Hall, dates from last century. This building offers a superb view on to the impressive cataract in the gully below. The river can be crossed by a narrow stone bridge giving a lovely view of the upper and lower reaches of this part of the River Bran.

This delightful area is a favourite spot for those seeking a peaceful stroll through very attractive woodland, and irrespective of the season, The Hermitage has a charm all of its own.

THE HERMITAGE, DUNKELD

B Y this time Miss Ritchie was beginning to feel tired and wondered if she should put off visiting her first home in the tenement block.

But she decided she may as well finish her tour. So she gave the driver another address and a little later the car pulled up outside a tenement building in a busy, working-class district on the north side of the town.

Slowly, very carefully, she mounted the stairs to the first-floor flat and she had to stop to draw breath before she rang the bell.

A young woman with a little girl peeping from behind her skirt answered her ring. Miss Ritchie, looking pale and still a little breathless, started to tell her why she was there when the young woman interrupted her.

"You're gey tired looking," she said, "I'm sure you could do with a cup of tea. Come on now." She put her free arm round Miss Ritchie's shoulders.

Once she'd sat down on a hard wooden chair at the white deal table, Miss Ritchie felt better.

"I was gasping for a cup of tea and I'm so grateful to you for asking me to come into your home. Especially when all I wanted to say was that about sixty years ago I was born in this house, and I just thought it would be nice to see it again before I . . . before I finish for the day."

"Well now, imagine that," said Mrs Turner. "What a lovely thought after all those years. And has it changed all that much?"

Miss Ritchie's eyes travelled to where the kitchen grate had been and where a small, one-bar, electric fire now stood, then on to the built-in bed where she'd first seen the light of day.

"No," she said, "it hasn't changed that much."

"I'm sorry my husband isn't in," said Mrs Turner. "He'd have been so glad to hear your story."

"He'll be out at his work?"

"I'm afraid not," Mrs Turner replied. "He hasn't worked for nearly two years now. He's just gone for a walk. He gets so fed-up just sitting here. It's hard for a young man."

"It certainly must be," Miss Ritchie said thoughtfully, and a few minutes later, having drunk her tea and listened to Mrs Turner's cheerful chatter she said her farewells and left.

Her hired car took her across town to her flat, where she collapsed with exhaustion on to her sofa.

I T took Miss Ritchie a few days to recover from so much excitement, then she phoned for her lawyer to come and visit her.

When he arrived, Miss Ritchie, as usual, didn't mince her words.

"Mr Hamilton," she said, "I'm going to die."

"I am sorry to hear that," replied Mr Hamilton, who had long since ceased to be surprised at the pronouncements of his clients.

"We must all die some time, Mr Hamilton. But I am going to die in three months' time."

"Three months!" the lawyer exclaimed, slightly taken aback this time. "How can you be sure?"

Miss Ritchie's Last Wish

"By habit and custom," said Miss Ritchie mysteriously. "It has been my practice to be exact in all things. I will die on the thirtieth of September. There are several undertakings which I want you to arrange, a week before my death, on the twenty-third of September."

On that day, at about ten-thirty in the morning a van drew up at Mrs Croft's bungalow home. Two men got out of the van and headed for the front door. Mrs Croft met them there.

"We have fifty rose bushes for you," one of the men told her.

"Not for me," she replied. "You've come to the wrong house."

"You are Mrs Croft?" he insisted, and he reeled off the right address.

"Yes that's me."

"Well, we have fifty rose bushes for you — all paid for. And we have to plant them, weed your garden and generally tidy up your lawn. We're to do this for the next ten years. It's all paid for in advance."

Mrs Croft stared at them in utter disbelief.

"I think I'd better sit down," she said shakily.

A T around the same time that morning another van drew up at Mrs Nelson's council house. Mrs Nelson was busy hanging up some washing.

"We've got a washing machine and a tumble drier for you," the delivery man said.

Mrs Nelson smiled.

"I'm afraid it must be another Mrs Nelson," she said. ▶ *p110*

GREAT BRITON

SIR ALEXANDER FLEMING

Born in 1881 at Loudoun in Ayrshire, Fleming was the bacteriologist who discovered the bacteria-killing properties of the fungus Penicillium notatum — by accident. However it wasn't until the Second World War that penicillin became a recognised antibiotic. In 1945 Fleming was joint winner of a Nobel prize.

Loudoun Hill

The man repeated the address, indicating there was no mistake. "And," he added, "we have four boys' bikes, too."

"You must be joking," she exclaimed.

"It's no joke. Everything's paid for, in advance."

"But who on earth would do a thing like that?" Mrs Nelson asked, shaking her head.

And on the same day the postman delivered a special letter to the tenement home of Mrs Turner. She opened it and stared with unbelieving eyes at the cheque she withdrew from the envelope.

"What is it?" her husband called. "Another bill?"

"No. It looks like one of these daft cheques you get through the post these days."

"Is it for a million pounds?" he queried.

"I haven't got my specs on, but it looks like ten pounds or maybe even a hundred pounds."

Mr Turner took the cheque from her.

"It's a cheque all right," he gasped, "and it's for ten thousand pounds! And it's not from the football pools — it's from a solicitor."

Mrs Turner sighed.

"The daft things have sent it to the wrong address. You'd better phone them."

Mr Turner did just that and he was assured that no mistake had been made. On his return from the phone box they both sat down at the white deal table and cried.

ON the twenty-ninth of September, Dr Bone called at the hospital where Miss Ritchie had been taken. He saw a small, shrivelled body lying under the sheets and he shook his head sadly. She had gone down so quickly at the end.

He approached the bed.

"Miss Ritchie, are you asleep?" he whispered.

Miss Ritchie struggled to open her eyes.

"What is today's date?" she asked quietly.

"It's September the twenty-ninth," he replied. "Is there anything I can do for you?"

"No, Doctor," she said. "I left things a little late, but I've done everything that has to be done. You can come back tomorrow." She closed her eyes again.

Dr Bone slipped quietly out of the room and as he glanced back he noticed a quiet smile of contentment on Miss Ritchie's face. □

Although one of Devon's main attractions to visitors is its famed cream teas, another is the picturesque tranquillity of many of its rural hamlets and villages. Charming thatched houses beside gently babbling brooks — like this one in Dartmoor — seem to breathe contentment. Warm-coloured stone and lush greenery make a serene picture in which time appears to stand completely still.

Peter Baker

BUCKLAND-IN-THE-MOOR, DEVON

BUILDING
on
LOVE

by ALICE MACKIE

T HE cake was the most perfect Edith Stevenson had ever made. It was her second term at the cake-icing class, and with her twenty-fifth wedding anniversary just round the corner, she had decided to make her own cake for the occasion.

"It need not be large," she explained to Mrs Baird, her teacher. "There's only my husband, two sons, one daughter-in-law and a new baby granddaughter, much too young even to sample the icing."

"You're one of my top pupils this term," Mrs Baird told her, admiring the cake whose delicate tracery of icing looked like beautifully-made lace. Only the smooth top remained to be decorated, and Edith had now brought that decoration from home. Mrs Baird's eyes popped when she saw it, and the other members of the class gathered round to appreciate the finished cake.

"Are you sure you want it like that, Mrs Stevenson?" the teacher asked.

"Quite sure," Edith told her, smiling, though her thoughts were winging back to that other cake, her wedding cake, which so nearly didn't get eaten at all.

She had been six years old

when she first met Laurence Stevenson, a tall, strong boy of ten who had little time to spare for the small daughter of his mother's best friend. As an only child, Edith was used to going everywhere with her mother, but a day came when Mrs Paterson had been obliged to go to the dentist and Edith was left in Mrs Stevenson's charge.

The day had been wet, she remembered, and she felt rather bad tempered at being abandoned by her mother, so that she had scowled fiercely at the big boy who was drawing a picture in his new drawing book. She was trying hard to keep the tears at bay.

"Can't you two play together?" Mrs Stevenson had demanded. "Now, Laurence, you be nice to Edith. She's only a little girl."

Laurence had sighed, then he found a small piece of wood and a knife. Soon Edith was fascinated to watch as he carved the wood into the shapes of small animals.

"You can have those," he said diffidently, giving her two, and she took them with shining eyes. Did one fall in love at six, she wondered. Many years later, when she was eighteen and Laurence twenty-two, it seemed to her that she had loved him all her life.

L AURENCE'S talent for drawing, painting and carving had remained with him during his growing years, and when the time came for him to study for a career, he was influenced by his family into choosing architecture. He loved the form and shape of buildings, old and new, and even when he and Edith went out for an afternoon, or out dancing in the evenings, Laurence's eyes swept over all forms of buildings whilst Edith preferred the soft beauty of growing things.

She could not remember a time when Laurence actually asked her to marry him. Somehow it was always understood that they would marry when Laurence finished his course and found a good job.

"It's a seven-year course, darling," he told her, after they became engaged. "It will be ages before I qualify."

"The time will soon pass," Edith told him comfortingly.

The small, pretty child had grown up into a beautiful young woman, and she was now taking a business course.

"Sometimes I wonder . . ." Laurence's voice tailed off, and his eyes were reflective.

"What?" she asked.

"Oh, I don't know . . . maybe architecture isn't really what I want."

"But you *love* buildings," Edith said, "and your parents are behind you all the way."

"I know." He sighed and turned away. "Perhaps that's part of the trouble."

Laurence liked to find a holiday job during his long summer vacation, in order to earn extra money to help him through each term. The following year a large building firm was granted a big project locally, and he was lucky enough to find a job on the site. Edith saw less of him than usual that summer.

Laurence loved everything about the building site, and no job was too

114

boring or harassing for him. He learned fast and Edith sighed as she resigned herself to listening to the fascinating details of the building trade. Fascinating to Laurence, that was. She did her best to take an interest, but when she could no longer stifle a yawn one evening, Laurence took her in his arms and kissed her.

"I'm sorry, darling," he told her as he leaned his chin against her soft dark hair. "I must be boring you. I hate having to wait so long for us to be married. I wish we could be married now . . . next week . . . next month, even. I would like to build a house second to none, where we would be happy together."

Edith nodded and her arms crept round his neck. She had thought the time would pass quickly, but it was very slow going indeed.

A T Christmas, Laurence put his knowledge of building to good effect when he offered to repair the inside walls of the church hall, and their minister looked at him doubtfully, then called a committee meeting, attended by Edith's father, who thought that Laurence could not make the walls worse than they were already. A fee was agreed, and Laurence was given the job.

"You'll never do it before you're due to return to university," Edith observed.

"Yes I will," Laurence said happily, exhilarated to be tackling the job. "They were thinking of asking the Manpower Services, but some of the men have agreed to help me, and I'll get the job done in double-quick time, see if I don't."

Edith bit her lip. "But . . . but I never see you, Laurence."

The weather had grown cold, and both had zipped themselves into warm anoraks and boots in order to go for a walk and be on their own for a little while.

"I know, darling. I've been wanting to talk to you seriously about that," Laurence said, taking her hand and tucking it under his arm. "I want to give up my course. I'm doing the wrong thing, Edith. I want to be a builder instead."

"A builder? Instead of an architect? Laurence, you must be out of your mind!"

"I won't be throwing all my studying away," he told her. "It's a great help with practical work. Mr Sloane, the general manager of Baxter's, is going to give me a chance, and I want to take it. There are plenty of architects training at university without me."

"Plenty of builders without you, too, Laurence," Edith said. "Aren't there thousands of them unemployed at the moment?"

"Not if you're in the right place at the right time, and really want to become a craftsman. I could do well. I could even have my own firm one day. The family finances wouldn't suffer. In fact, we could be married very soon, Edith. We could afford it."

F OR a while she rested in his arms, then she pushed him away. Surely there was no comparison between the skill he had in him to become and architect, and the skill to be a builder. She knew little enough about it, but wouldn't his parents be heart-broken? Would they blame her for not wanting to wait to be married?

Laurence felt her withdrawal and his eyes hardened a little. "You don't approve?" he asked.

GREAT BRITON

CHARLES MACINTOSH

The inventor of the "mackintosh" raincoat was Scottish chemist Charles Macintosh who was born in Glasgow in 1766. In 1823 he developed a process for waterproofing fabric with a rubber film. By 1836 waterproof coats became widely known as mackintoshes.

"What do your parents say?"

"It's *my* life . . . *our* life, not theirs," he said, quietly. "Edith?"

She stared at him unhappily. "Oh, I don't know, Laurence," she said. "It seems . . . well . . ."

"That you might prefer to be the wife of an architect than the wife of a builder?" His voice was suddenly rough and she might have sensed his disappointment if his words had not made her so angry.

"No!" she cried. "How can you think that? I don't care what you do. I mean . . ."

"Don't you?" he asked. "It seems to me you care very much indeed."

"I'm only thinking of you, Laurence, you'll regret it for the rest of your life if you give up your course now."

This time he made no reply, and with one accord they turned and began to retrace their footsteps home.

"I'll be busy tomorrow at the church hall," Laurence told her diffidently, when they arrived back at Edith's home.

"Don't worry, I know," she said stiffly. "I hope you enjoy the work."

There was no-one at home and Edith was thankful to be on her own for once as the tears began to slide down her cheeks. What a thing to quarrel about! How could she ever make Laurence understand how she felt?

"Is that you, Edith?" A voice from the doorway startled her, and she whirled round to see a friend of her mother's staring in at her. She had no time to disguise her swollen face before Lorna Campbell walked into the room.

"Oh, my dear!" she said with sympathy. "What has happened?"

"N . . . nothing, Aunt Lorna. I'm OK."

"Well, you don't look it." Lorna told her, drawing back a little from the girl. "If you don't want to tell me, though, I'll understand. It's probably none of my business."

Edith gave a shuddering sigh. "No, I don't mind your knowing. I'm at odds with Laurence at the moment. He . . . he wants to give up his architecture course and become a builder instead. He wants us to get married now . . . at least he did. I don't think he's very pleased with me at the moment, but I'm so afraid he's throwing his life away. I've told him my opinion."

L ORNA sat down beside her godchild. She wanted to put her arms round the girl, but Edith was now a very independent young lady and Lorna was not sure if she would respond.

"The one thing I have learned in my longish life," she said slowly, "is that no-one can live another person's life for them. How can you decide for Laurence, dear? How can his father or mother decide? Close as you are to him, you can't possibly know how he feels. You can't jump into his skin and know all his feelings, can you? He must want to be a builder very much, or he wouldn't do this. It would be so much easier to please you, and his parents, wouldn't it?"

Edith's sobs subsided, and she moved a little on the settee. "I . . . I suppose you're right, Aunt Lorna. Come to think of it, I don't like having people decide for me, either."

She sat quietly for a few minutes, while Lorna waited.

"It would be nice to be married. Laurence is sure we can manage on the money he could earn. He says he'll paint pictures and carve his little animals in his spare time. I . . . I think I'll go and phone him, Aunt Lorna."

There was no reply from Laurence's number, and he had already left the house when Edith tried again the following morning. She had no time to try again before she left for work, though the idea of an early wedding had begun to grow like a flower in her heart. It would be wonderful, she admitted. She would tell Laurence so.

Love for him washed over her and she went off to work with a song in her heart. Laurence had always loved buildings. He loved the materials as much as the design, and he would make a wonderful builder, and a very fine craftsman indeed.

It was not until her half-day that Edith saw him again, and when she did, it seemed as though there was a stranger in his place as he worked steadily on the church hall repairs.

"Come to read me another lecture?" he asked, and there was no smile of welcome on his face. "If so, I don't want to hear it. I've had enough from my father, though I think he sees reason now."

E DITH felt a lump rising in her throat. His tone was so brusque and there was no love in his eyes when he looked at her. Had she lost Laurence's love? It was something she had always taken for granted because he seemed to have been taking care of her ever since he first carved his small wooden animals for her.

"No, I came to say you were right," she managed to say at length. "If you want to be a builder, well, I don't mind."

"Big of you!" he said roughly. "You don't mind until the next time you decide that I'm spoiling both our lives. No, Edith, I've been doing a lot of thinking, too."

Laurence jumped down the two rungs of the ladder he had been using. "Perhaps I'm being selfish to shape my life without reference to you. Perhaps I'm not right for you."

Edith could hardly speak for the pain in her heart, yet she also had a fierce pride. If Laurence had changed his mind and did not want her, then she would not plead her own cause. There was nothing so dead as dead love.

"Very well, Laurence, if that's how you feel," she said hoarsely. "I . . . I wish you all the luck in the world."

Almost blindly she turned away, keeping her eyes to the ground so that he would not see the tears. It was through those tears that she suddenly saw a tiny grey mouse rushing out of the wainscoting where Laurence had been working, and making straight for her legs. Edith loved a wooden mouse which Laurence had carved for her, but a live one was something very different.

With a scream she suddenly threw herself into Laurence's arms. "Oh, Laurence, there . . . there's a mouse," she babbled. "Don't let it come near me. I'm terrified of them. Don't let it run up my leg . . ."

Laurence was laughing softly as he held her, though her arms were wound tightly round his neck.

"It's only a baby," he whispered. "It's gone home to its mother. I'm afraid the caretaker will be setting his traps again. I've disturbed a few of his mice while I've been working here."

He kissed her, and Edith leaned against him until her heart hammered a little less.

"Oh, Laurence," she said. "What a fright!"

"Don't go away," he told her. "I'm falling down on the job, but I don't care. I'm sorry, darling, but you must know I'll always love you, and you come first with me."

"It's a great idea if we get married soon," Edith said happily. "I don't care what you do so long as we belong to each other, and you're happy in the work you choose to do."

NOW, as she produced a small sugar mouse and placed it on top of the Silver Wedding cake, Mrs Baird could not resist a good laugh.

"That's a new one on me," she said. "A mouse on a cake."

"There was a mouse on my wedding cake, too," Edith said reminiscently. "I got my Aunt Lorna to cover a wee wooden one with almond paste then icing, and we popped it on top of the cake. I've still got it, and I nearly brought it along for this cake, but I was afraid you would faint at the sight of it! As I nearly did, once, when I saw a real one . . ." □

by
ELIZA
YEAMAN

Behind A Daughter's Tears

H ANNAH gazed in wonder at the silvery white snowflake on the palm of her blue, woolly mitten. The snowflake was like a tiny piece of magic, and it was her very own. She had not made a very good job of painting a snowflake in the nursery school this afternoon. She knew that it was not good because the teacher had said so with a smile.

"Well, you tried, Hannah." And she had pinned Hannah's snowflake on a part of the wall behind the piano.

119

Hannah had not cried, but she'd felt very sad because her paintings were usually good enough to go on the big part of the wall beside the door so that when people were playing they could always see the lovely bright colours she had chosen.

GREAT BRITON

WILLIAM PATERSON

The founder of The Bank Of England was a Scotsman, William Paterson, who was born in Dumfries in 1658. Paterson's plan was to establish a national bank formed by merchants who raised money from shareholders. This money was lent to King William III who then granted the bank the right to issue notes to the value of the cash lent, creating what is today Britain's entirely government-owned central bank.

She hadn't really liked painting this afternoon when she had been allowed to use only white paint. How could white be pretty, she'd thought. But now, when she saw the real snowflake on her hand, she thought that white was beautiful. Then another snowflake landed, and another. Hannah smiled, entranced. Her legs seemed to want to dance for joy. Yet she daren't move, in case the magical snowflakes were lost.

"Hannah! Must you always dawdle? Come on!" Sybil Cargill grasped her small daughter's hand and drew her firmly across the road, into the car park then into the car. Every night it was a rush to collect Hannah and drive home before the traffic became so thick that the ten-minute journey was liable to take half an hour. If only Hannah would co- operate, she thought every night, it would be so much easier.

She could run or skip or walk quickly any other time, Sybil thought, as she lifted the child into the back of the car and deposited the shopping bags beside her. Then, just as she started to close the door, she realised that Hannah was crying.

"What's wrong, darling?" Sybil spoke in tones of mixed exasperation and concern. "Why are you crying?"

"You made me lose my snowflakes I caught," Hannah wailed accusingly.

"I'm sorry, pet." Sybil sighed and reached for the tissue box. She tried to coax away the tears by saying, "There are plenty more snowflakes —

Mummy will have to swish them away with the windscreen wipers."

As far as Sybil was concerned, the falling snow was another trouble added to the many. But at least Hannah cheered up a little and took a lively interest in the flakes which managed to cling to the windscreen.

Spring Morning

THE sun arose, a shining golden ball,
That April morning, cool and clear
and still.
The daffodils were standing green and
tall,
And mist — all white — was rolling
down the hill.
Then came a shower of rain which kissed
the earth
And sunshine made the raindrops
diamond bright.
The rain was Mother Nature's aid to
birth.
As buds began to bluster into sight.
The gold and purple crocuses stood
guard
Along the edge of borders round the
town.
The earth was smelling sweet — no
longer hard,
As, frost forgotten, spring had donned
her gown.
The winter now was just a memory past
And golden days and warmth were here
at last.

— *Kathleen Smalley.*

ON the way into the house, Hannah managed to catch some more snowflakes. But when she tried to show them to her two big brothers they had vanished.

"That's only water," Christopher said as he looked at her glove, "I don't believe you ever had snowflakes."

"I did! I did!" Hannah protested. "They flew down out of the sky."

"Did they have wings then?" Christopher asked.

Hannah sensed that he was teasing her and she looked at him uncertainly, tears welling up in her eyes. "No . . . they didn't have wings."

Nine-year-old Christopher was grinning now as he asked her, "So how did they manage to fly down out of the sky?"

At that point, eleven-year-old Robert took pity on his little sister and said, "Come on, Hannah, sit beside me. There's a cartoon coming on the TV in a minute."

"But she's got wingless birds on her glove!" Christopher exclaimed. "Don't let her sit beside you!"

"Give over." Robert put Hannah's mitten in front of the fire to dry, and told his brother, "Leave her alone, you clown."

"Who are you calling a clown?" Christopher gave Robert a push which sent him sprawling. Robert grabbed Christopher's legs and pulled him down . . .

Hannah backed away as they began to wrestle. Then she opened the door and called upstairs as loudly as she could. "Rachel! Rachel! The boys are fighting!"

Sixteen-year-old Rachel had gone straight upstairs to her room after school. She had exams coming up in a couple of weeks and she needed peace to study. She threw down her book and went to the top of the stairs.

She was annoyed with Hannah for disturbing her. But before she could say so, the front door opened and their father came in, shaking the snow off his jacket.

Hannah ran to him to be lifted into his arms and hugged as they exchanged delighted comments about the snow.

Paul Cargill had not enjoyed driving home in a blizzard, but his tiny daughter's excitement was infectious — it seemed necessary and natural to pretend that he was pleased.

GREAT BRITON

MRS BEETON

The author of the famous Book Of Household Management, Mrs Beeton, was born Isabella Mayson in Cheapside, London, in 1836. The idea for her book came about when she realised that no-one had written a good book to help new brides to manage the home. Her book, which took some four years to write, was phenomenally successful and new editions had to be produced. Isabella married a publisher, Samuel Beeton, when she was twenty. Sadly, however, her life was a short one — she died at the age of twenty-eight. But the name of Mrs Beeton lives on in her famous cookery writings.

"If there's lots of snow, can we build a snowman?" Hannah was asking.

"Sure we can . . ." Paul was smiling as he kissed her silky blonde head. But he paused, startled, as he looked up to find his older daughter watching the happy scene from the top of the stairs.

On Rachel's face there was a cold, scornful expression. His eyebrows lowered and he was about to say something when she turned swiftly away.

THE slam of her bedroom door sent a pang of dismay like an arrow into his heart. Only yesterday, it seemed, Rachel had cuddled him and kissed him as Hannah was doing. But now Rachel had no time for him. He thought that he had never known such hurt as that look on her face had caused.

"Tea's ready! Clean hands everybody, please." Sybil called out to the family in her usual brisk way. It was foolish, she knew, to act normal when her heart was breaking. But she didn't know what would happen if she let go of the tight rein she was keeping on her emotions.

It was almost nine o'clock when she went quietly into Rachel's bedroom.

"Hannah and the boys are asleep," she said, and added, "I just came to tell you I'm going out — I won't be much more than an hour."

In astonishment, Rachel asked, "Where are you going?"

Sybil could not control the flush which stained her cheeks, nor did she meet her daughter's eyes as she replied. "I'm only going to see Granny and Grandpa. I shan't be very long."

She knew that she ought to have made the effort to smile, to say something reassuring before she closed the door and hurried downstairs. Rachel was a sensitive girl, she must be aware that there was something seriously wrong. But unfortunately, Sybil knew that words of comfort right now would do nothing to cushion the blow which would soon strike not only Rachel but the entire family.

Before she rang her parents' doorbell, Sybil made a valiant attempt to compose herself, and to collect her thoughts. But tears were inevitable from the moment she told her shocked parents what had been happening to her marriage — Paul had been seeing another woman.

"I've suspected for a while," Sybil said, "then last Tuesday, I had proof —" Her voice broke as she went on, sobbing. "I knew then I couldn't close my eyes to it — I have too much pride."

Her parents were kind and sympathetic. They would support her in every way they could. They agreed with her decision to confront her husband with her knowledge of his affair.

Sybil was grateful to them. But as she drove home alone, through the snow, the confined space of the car and the darkness seemed to heighten the feeling of isolation. This could be a foretaste of the years to come, she told herself, the years without Paul.

She could not remember a time when she had not loved Paul, adored him, worshipped him. Seventeen, almost eighteen years of marriage had not lessened the love which was part of her. The very prospect of a separation from him seemed to tear at the roots of her heart. How would she survive without him?

Then there were the children to consider. Sybil's heart told her that she must keep all four of them. But her head was reminding her that they had a right to choose which of their parents they wanted to live with. Rachel, she thought, had always loved her father best . . .

RACHEL was downstairs in the kitchen when her mother arrived home and she offered at once to make some supper.

"Only coffee for me, then," Sybil said, and then she added as kindly as she could, "You take yours upstairs will you? I'm not much in the mood for talking."

For once, Rachel did not argue. She did not feel like making small talk either, partly because she was afraid that she might blurt out the words which she had resolved not to say.

Some friends had seen her father with another woman. Rachel had tried to laugh it off when she was told. It was not possible — not her father. But then she'd been told again, and again . . . It was as if school mates whom she'd thought of as friends turned into enemies as they plied her with information and watched her reactions.

Rachel knew that she was immature and rather shy. She went to the occasional disco, but unlike many in her age group she did not go to night clubs and other adult entertainments. She felt that she could wait to sample these when she was older. She was not enticed by the thrill of making up to look over eighteen.

However, in recent weeks she had begun to feel immeasurably older and wiser. She felt betrayed by her friends as well as her father.

She carried a mug of coffee through to her mother who was slumped in a chair in the lounge. She had never seen her mother looking so sad.

"Thanks, Rachel," Sybil spoke absently, "you are a darling."

"So are you, Mum." Rachel fought against the tears which burned at the back of her eyes. She stooped for a brief moment to hug her mother before she ran upstairs to her room, leaving her supper forgotten in the kitchen.

Sybil sighed, thinking that the tension in the atmosphere had obviously communicated itself already to Rachel. She dreaded to imagine what things would be like when they discovered the truth.

But even more, Sybil was dreading the looming confrontation with her husband. She stood up and drank her coffee as she waited and watched at the window for him.

SNOW was still falling softly. The world outside had a haunting, mysterious beauty which brought an ache to her heart and tears to her eyes.

Upstairs in her little room, Hannah wakened in the darkness and smiled sleepily when she looked towards the window. There would be plenty of snow in the morning for her big snowman. She had a hat and scarf waiting to put on him and two marbles for his eyes and a carrot for his nose and a piece of orange peel for his mouth.

She was dreaming about the snowman when she wakened again. Mummy and Daddy must have the TV turned up too loud, she thought drowsily, and snuggled further down into her cosy bed.

Everything was silent when she woke up again. She would have to get up soon and get dressed to go to nursery school. Then she remembered that it was Saturday, and as she woke up fully, she remembered about the snowman and jumped up and ran to the window. Yes! There was lots and lots of snow! She ran at once to tell her daddy.

But her daddy was not in his bed beside Mummy. Mummy looked at the clock and said grumpily, "Hannah, go back to sleep. It's not nearly time to get up."

"Where's Daddy?" Hannah whispered. But Mummy was covering her face and did not answer.

Hannah went slowly into her sister's room and Rachel immediately turned on to her other side and said sternly, "Go back to bed, Hannah."

Hannah closed the door and went into her brothers' room. Christopher was lying on his back snoring and Robert was hidden under the quilt. There was no sign of her father.

Hannah walked barefoot to the top of the stairs. Then she paused — she had been told to go back to bed and she was an obedient child . . . Silent tears rolled down her cheeks as she sat down on the top step and began to cry, so heavily she felt she'd burst.

Paul Cargill was lying on the sofa in the lounge. He had been awake all night, he thought. But he must have dozed off eventually because daylight had come and he could hear the sound of someone weeping.

He threw off the tartan rug which covered him and swung his feet to the floor and padded across to the door still dazed and heavy with lack of sleep.

"Hannah?" He spoke his little daughter's name as he started up the stairs towards her.

"Daddy!" Hannah's forlorn, pathetic posture was suddenly transformed as she stood up and launched herself into his arms. But her tears continued to flow as she hugged him ecstatically.

"I couldn't find you, Daddy. I looked in every bed and I couldn't find you."

Paul sat down on the stairs and cradled her in his arms, kissing her tears away. But he knew that a few tears of his own were mingling with hers as he soothed her with soft words. "It's all right, Daddy's here," he murmured. "Daddy will always be here, don't cry little love, don't cry."

SOON, Hannah's tears were only diamond glints on her eyelashes. She would forget this morning when she could not find her daddy. Instead she would remember this as the day of the snowman. But her father knew that he would never forget the desolate child weeping at the top of the stairs. For her tears had finally brought him back to his senses.

He sent Hannah to dress up warmly while he went to his wife, to humbly beg her forgiveness.

"I've been a fool," he said. "I love you, Sybil, I've never stopped loving you . . ."

Hannah stood in the doorway with all the bits and pieces for the snowman in her hand and she said in her bossiest, most reproving voice, "Daddy! Will you please stop kissing Mummy or we shall never get my snowman built!"

Rachel sat up quickly when she heard her small sister's order — and the laughter of her parents which followed.

Late last night she had fallen asleep covering her ears to shut out the sounds of the bitter row between her parents when her father had arrived home. But now her heart lifted, they were obviously on good terms again. Perhaps they hadn't been true, these things she'd heard. Or perhaps they were no longer true.

She lay down again, knowing instinctively that the continuing murmur of voices and the soft laughter was bringing her life back to normal. She was glad now that she had not told her mother what she knew.

Downstairs Hannah and her father were hastily swallowing some cornflakes and milk to give them enough energy to build the snowman.

The boys came out a little while later. They would make a bigger snowman, they boasted. But Hannah was not in competition with her brothers. She knew that she and her daddy were making the best snowman in the world. □

125

Rosa and Romance

by KATE HANNAH

TO say to my Rosa's face that she was a bit of an actress who delighted in playing romantic rôles, might have resulted in wild protestations — but it was true enough. If I'd not loved her so dearly, I would never have suffered those "performances" of hers for so long.

We'd been courting for six long years and that, in itself, had been no mean feat. To reach Rosa's home meant I had to walk around the entire valley to the farm she shared with her parents.

Twenty-four years old, Rosa looked years younger with her long, flowing brown hair, dimpled cheeks and a pair of startlingly blue eyes that could melt the most stubborn man's heart. Oh, I loved my Rosa all right, and her parents, Joe and Martha Patrick, were well aware of it.

Indeed, two years before, I'd actually persuaded Rosa to wear my engagement ring which once belonged to my grandmother and boasted a large ruby which would wink at me provocatively each time she performed her fluttery evasive act.

"But, Johnnie dear, I'm not ready to marry you yet. For a start, how would my poor parents manage without me?"

Very well indeed, I wanted to yell at her, and it was true enough. The Patricks were one of the fittest couples who worked the valley, labouring all the hours God sent on a farm almost identical to mine.

"You will still be saying that, Rosa, when my hair has turned grey and I'm so stiff I won't be able to walk the two miles round the valley. I tell you, Rosa, you must make up your mind soon, or else I'll . . ."

Well, I'd ask myself, what would I do? Leave her at home, an "old maid" to browse amongst the lost treasures she so meticulously packed into that bottom drawer of hers? There was this red tablecloth, for instance. Now I'd been with Rosa the day she bought the material, on one of our rare visits to the city. A square of scarlet linen, she chose, and a box stacked with silk threads to go with it.

It was to be her most adventurous effort yet, she told me excitedly, as the assistant wrapped it up. In actual fact, that red tablecloth became a bone of contention each time I walked round the valley to visit.

I watched her sew every one of those blasted white daisies, garlands of them around the edge, neat bunches tied with ribbon dotted elsewhere. Many's the time I felt like snatching the needle from her hand and retorting, "Rosa, it's you I want, not some daft fancy tablecloth."

Now it was completed, and to add fuel to the fire, she would produce it each Thursday when I was invited round to dine with her family. The thing would be worn out by the time we were wed.

IT was Rosa's father who finally came up with the solution. I admit it freely — I have never been blessed by a lively imagination.

"You're too patient by far, Johnnie," he said to me one night when we'd stepped out on the porch for a quiet smoke. "Play that girl of mine at her own game. If she wants a bit of drama in her life then let her have it. Set Rosa an ultimatum. That should soon get things moving."

"But what if she calls my bluff?" I protested. "I love Rosa, and could never be happy with anyone else."

Joe frowned at me. "I believe you, lad, but don't you think that girl of ours knows it, too? It's all a fine act. Remember how we sent Rosa to those ballet lessons, Martha and me? Well, it was the worst thing we ever did. They chose her to play the dying swan, and she still fancies herself in that rôle. But you ruffle her feathers, Johnnie lad, and she'll soon come floating ashore." He was a droll man was Joe Patrick.

I thought about his advice all the way home through the valley. Now I should mention here that our valley itself is a truly remarkable place. Tourists visit regularly. They call it something of a curiosity, for if one stands at one side of it and calls out "Halloo" then the sound will echo round and round its steep walls for ages. Feeling slightly adventurous that night, I tried it out for sound with a soft "Rosa" and nearly jumped out of my skin, for the name rustled back to me again and again, until it became almost a prayer.

Thursday evenings had always been set aside for me to trudge round the valley and eat supper with Rosa and her folk. They went out of their way to make me feel welcome. Well, when I arrived that following Thursday, I found Rosa perched as usual on the rail of their veranda, looking particularly desirable.

She wore a wide-skirted white dress with a scarlet belt at its waist, and for a moment I thought she might easily slip on to the lake and perform her favourite rôle. Somehow the sight of this languid pose hardened my resolve.

All through supper Rosa watched me curiously. Perhaps this was because I had merely dropped a light kiss on her cheek on arrival, instead of my usual warm embrace.

Joe sent me a knowing look, and at last, I gave an answering nod. He understood immediately and as soon as supper was over, he touched Martha's arm. "You and me, Martha, we're taking a turn up to the old mill tonight. My legs feel a mite stiff from sitting."

Martha looked a bit startled by the suggestion. She was a rotund little woman, not given to unnecessary exercise, and as she was about to protest, her good man took hold of one of her elbows and more or less prised her out of her seat and through the back door.

S O now, Rosa and I were quite alone, sitting on opposite sides of the fire. I watched a sleepy smile pass across her face and knew exactly what was going on in her mind. *Now my Johnnie will call me across and I'll perch on his knee and we'll sit nice and comfy, staring into the fire and dreaming of the future.*

A fair enough preoccupation it had been in the past, but not tonight. Certainly not tonight, for I had an ultimatum to deliver. "Rosa," I spoke ever so firmly. "I have something important to say to you. Now don't interrupt until I've finished." I took a long, deep breath. "Rosa, you and I must get married."

I watched her lips part as if to proclaim their usual protest. "Not one word until I'm finished talking, Rosa," I reminded her. "Now, I've spoken with your dad, and he assures me he and Martha can manage the farm perfectly well without you, and, if need be, they will hire a lass from the village to give Martha a hand in the kitchen. Now that just leaves the arrangements. I've spoken to the vicar and he's agreed to set aside Saturday the twenty-fourth — that's four weeks come this weekend, and I think that'll give you ample time to iron out that trousseau of yours."

She jumped to her feet, her hand movements panicky. She began to clear away the supper dishes, finally folding the scarlet tablecloth with its white daisies and placing it on top of the sideboard, then as she was about to pass by my chair, I imprisoned one of her wrists.

"Now I don't want your answer right now, Rosa. I tell you what you must do. You know that it takes me forty-five minutes to walk round the valley home?" She nodded silently. "And you know how you're able to watch me walk almost every inch of that way, from your porch?"

Once more, the solemn nod. "Well, Rosa love, I shall allow you exactly that time to make up your mind. Then you have to send me some signal. You may send it in whichever way you wish, only you must let me know, one way or the other, whether you intend to marry me four weeks come Saturday, or whether we should say goodbye."

I remember congratulating myself silently when I'd finished my ultimatum. If that was not dramatic enough for Rosa, I'd eat my cap. She did not say one word, just stood there as if she'd taken stage fright and forgotten her lines.

When it came time to say good night, she walked with me to the porch, where we stood close together. Rosa looked all soft and inviting. This moment had become one of the highlights of my weekly walk around the valley. Tonight, I told myself, be strong.

"Remember, Rosa. A sign — and before I reach the lip."

THEN I went striding out into the night, my steps with a sudden spring to them — at least until I'd gone a few hundred yards. It was then that the thought struck me. Joe Patrick and his daft ultimatums. What if Rosa were really to call my bluff and turn me down?

A couple of times I glanced furtively back and could see her still standing in the porch, her white dress illuminated by the light over the door. As I walked along the rim of the valley I strained my ears to catch the first sound, an echo perhaps, that would supply me with the reply to my ultimatum.

Could there, perhaps, be a bit of the romantic in me too, I asked myself. Fancy arranging something as daft as this! What sign would she give me anyway? I imagined it would appeal to my Rosa's love of drama for her to wait until I was on the far side of the valley, straight opposite her house, then I'd hear her sweet voice echo across. "I llove . . . llove . . . llove . . . you . . . John.nie.nie.nie." But, oh dear Lord, what if her answer was something else? What if she called out "Goodbye . . . aye . . . aye . . . aye . . . aye!"

I could not bear to think about that, and now I'd reached the spot directly opposite the Patricks' farmhouse and I could see that the lights still blazed, but there was no sign of Rosa on the porch. My heart sunk as, one by one, those lights went out. First Joe and Martha's bedroom light, then the one on the landing. Now the parlour light dimmed and all that was left was the one above the porch shining across at me like a warning beacon.

I had reached the lip of the valley now and a few more steps would take me over it and out of sight. I stopped again and strained my eyes, held my head to one side so my ears could pick up the faintest echo, then I watched the thin shaft of light as the door into the porch opened and there she stood, my Rosa, still wearing her white dress, but this time with something scarlet draped across her shoulders.

I watched as she whipped this off now and I could make out that it was the scarlet tablecloth which had adorned the supper table earlier. Then I waited, fascinated, as Rosa raised the red cloth above her head. One last dramatic gesture, I told myself. But what did her signal mean? A waved goodbye?

Then I heard the sound as it came echoing round the valley: "I will . . ll . . ll . . . Johnnie . . nie . . nie . . . nie!"

THEY were the words she would repeat in church four weeks later and there were our respective parents watching us approvingly, and no doubt sighing with relief.

Romantic? Ah, well, I suppose you might call it that, but then courting some thirty-odd years ago was meant to be a rather special time, something to recall in the years to come. Women such as my Rosa had to have something out of the ordinary to remember, especially when life became a fairly humdrum affair, feeding hens, milking cows, fetching the milk home frozen in the pail when winter came to our valley.

☆　　　☆　　　☆　　　☆

Tonight, Rosa and I sit by our roaring fire and I listen as she remonstrates with our youngest girl, Tina, who is at present an art student living in the city. Tina has just dropped a bombshell. She informs us that she intends to move into a flat shortly with three other students. Nothing remarkable about that, you may say, but then Tina happens to mention that two of her flatmates will be lads.

"But, Mum," Tina protests in that matter-of-fact voice of hers, "it is simply a matter of economics. This way, our grants will last out."

As I study young Tina's face, I marvel at how much she resembles the "earlier" Rosa. There, however, any resemblance stops, for Tina has no stage part to play. To her, life is real and earnest.

The boy, who has brought her to the farm tonight on the pillion of his motorbike, is called Ronnie. He's an open-faced lad who assures me that he intends to become a surveyor some day. Apparently, he seems terribly fond of our girl, whereas Tina seems to have her sights fixed firmly on a career.

At last, the young pair screech off around the valley and the sound of Ronnie's machine will echo back for hours to haunt us. Rosa sighs and comes across to perch herself on the arm of my chair. I knock out my pipe on the hearth and study my wife carefully. Rosa, the mother of our five children, has grown round and rosy, just like her mother, Martha, but still has a faraway look in her eyes on occasion, a look that can cause my heart to beat faster.

"Changed days, eh Johnnie?" She speaks at last, her voice tinged by regret. Now she rests her head on my shoulder. "A matter of economics indeed."

As I am wont to do on the odd occasion when we have the house to ourselves, I draw Rosa on to my knee and begin to stroke her hair.

"Give her time, pet," I assure her fondly. "One of these days, she'll discover her own red tablecloth." □

by GRACE MACAULAY

A Grandma
In A Million

"NO, Danny, you can *not* have tea," Clare Conway told her small son firmly. "Drink up your milk now."

Normally, she would have coaxed him to drink his milk, making a little game of it, but tonight her patience was being severely tested and her nerves were fraying.

It was obvious to Clare that Danny must have been allowed to drink tea at his grandmother's house. It wouldn't do him any harm, Clare knew, but after his long bout of sore throats and colds, Danny badly needed building up with nourishing drinks as well as a healthy diet.

But right now, Clare made no comment, partly because she knew Danny would leap immediately to his grandmother's defence, but mainly because she was certain that Jack, her husband, would chortle in that maddening way of his and make yet another remark about what he called their great rivalry for Danny's love.

Clare didn't find his comments amusing; she wasn't about to give him the satisfaction of being right, she would wait and remind Julia, Danny's grandmother, later about the tea. In the meantime, she reached for a slice of bread and began to butter it.

"Shall I spread one for you?" she asked Danny pleasantly.

"Not with butter." Danny wrinkled his nose and then lifted a piece of bread and took a bite of it.

"Have some jam," his father said, moving the dish and spooning a generous portion on to his son's bread. "There now, can you spread it with your knife?"

Danny gave a deep sigh and started to smooth out the jam, somehow managing to scrape most of it on to the plate and some on to the tablecloth.

Clare looked away from the mess rather pointedly. It was half past six, he would be going up for his bath soon. Perhaps with a bit of luck

they would get through the next hour without any more friction — and hopefully the bad habits he seemed to pick up at his grandmother's would be forgotten by the morning.

Then her hopes were dashed as she heard Danny pleading with his father to allow him to come downstairs again after his bath, instead of going to bed.

"Only for five minutes, Daddy." Danny's smile held a world of appeal, and he promised persuasively, "I'll read a whole page of my reading book to you."

Jack glanced at Clare, who pursed her lips and shook her head — which only meant that now Jack was adding his entreaties to Danny's. She had to give in, but she was not at all pleased. She knew better than anyone how easily her son could spin five minutes out into half an hour at least.

B UT the threat of changing her mind did help to keep him from dawdling too long over his bath. When he tried to insist on having a cold shower to rinse off the soap, Clare merely held open his bath towel and smiled.

"I thought you wanted to spend some time downstairs with Daddy?"

Naturally, Danny was dried and powdered and into his pyjamas and dressing-gown in record time. He was even eager to put on his slippers which now sported a large scorch mark on each toe.

"We must get you a new pair," Clare said.

"Oh, no, Mummy. I still like these," Danny said earnestly. "Granny says they have character now," he told her proudly.

She ought to know, Clare thought acidly as Danny dashed away downstairs. She was the one who put them too near her electric fire. But there was no point in being angry about it any more, Clare thought — especially as Jack had been the one to tackle his mother about that particular episode.

At the time he had gone as far as to say that Danny would not be permitted to spend the night with his grandmother again since she was so careless.

Julia had been rather subdued, admitting that perhaps it was spoiling the child to warm his little slippers, but after all, she was only a grandmother . . .

Later it transpired that her dog must have pushed the slippers too close to the fire. It made Clare even angrier to think that Julia would rather accept the blame herself then let her beloved brute be criticised.

Normally Clare was very fond of dogs, but she'd complained to Jack about Julia's.

"That poor animal has been absolutely ruined. Nobody can go near it except your mother. I'm terrified it may bite Danny."

"It has no teeth." Jack would grin at her. "But that's a pity — a smart nip might keep Danny from teasing her."

Clare would deny that Danny teased the dog, which would make Jack say that she was obviously blind to her son's faults. And the argument would end there for the time being.

Clare turned down Danny's bed and switched on his lamp. Why was there always trouble when the child returned from his grandmother's? Was it her own fault? Clare wondered.

But no, it was not, she assured herself. She wasn't an unreasonable person. She used to get along very well with Julia, but that was before Daniel was born.

She went downstairs, dispirited by the conflict within her, yet resolute in the knowledge that it was her duty as Danny's mother to ensure that he was properly brought up. Nobody likes spoiled children, she reminded herself. It was best for Danny to have established rules and sensible discipline.

H E was sitting on his father's lap, but he scrambled down, giving his mother an angelic smile, followed by a bear hug and a smacking kiss.

"I'll go up to bed by myself tonight," he assured Clare. "And Daddy says he will come up later and put my light out."

"Are you planning some mischief, Danny Conway?" Clare asked him.

"No, I'll be very careful. And I'll be sure to put the top back on my pen when I've finished writing."

Clare let him go, but she turned to Jack.

"What have you two been cooking up?"

The London Pigeon

A S lovely as a lilac-spray,
  As soft as thistledown,
In bright-eyed beauty every day
You wing your charming, cheerful way
Through dusty London Town.

Your country cousins would disdain
The tumult and the throng,
As, in some chequered country lane,
Or dreaming wood, or field of grain,
They croon their little song.

But you are with us everywhere,
By traffic undeterred,
So loyal, so satisfied to share
Our bread, our buns, our smoky air,
You iridescent bird.

In alley-ways, on office walls,
On tenement and tower,
There in the shadow of St Paul's,
Or strutting through the market stalls,
Like some pale-petalled flower.

As lovely as a lilac-spray,
As soft as thistledown,
I care not what the planners say,
May we never see the day
They banish you from Town!
— Kathleen O'Farrell.

"Nothing much," Jack replied casually. "He wants to write a letter to the paper." He picked up the newspaper and showed her. "I was reading this when he came down — and he was interested. He likes competitions."

Clare looked at the caption.

Do you have a granny in a million — write and tell the editor . . .

135

Jack crumpled the paper before she could read any more and laughed uproariously.

"Now you'll really have cause to be jealous!"

Clare shrugged and gave him a disdainful look, but as she marched out to the kitchen, there was moisture in her eyes and a mysterious ache in her heart.

Jack's smile faded into rather a wry grimace as he smoothed out the paper and started to fill in the crossword puzzle. He was sorry he had upset Clare. It was a bit unfair to tease her, but he knew that if he hadn't made some sort of joke he would by now be listening to a whole catalogue of complaints about his mother spoiling Danny.

He knew, because by now he recognised the signs — the long-suffering looks, the tight lips, the battle gleam in the eye.

Sometimes she started on about his mother the very moment Danny was in bed; and tonight he couldn't be bothered listening. He'd already endured a session with his mother, Julia, who wanted him to point out to Clare that Danny ought to be a bit fatter, and perhaps taller for his age. He didn't, in his grandmother's opinion, get enough exercise . . .

Jack heaved another sigh and attempted to give his mind to the crossword, but he couldn't stop thinking about the utter futility of the constant battle between his wife and his mother. It wouldn't be so bad if he wasn't always in the middle as they tossed their little darts at him, urging him to aim them at each other.

He was astonished by the strength of feeling which went into their criticisms, and it astonished him, too, that pleasant, ordinary women could be so jealous of each other.

IT had all started from the first day that Danny was brought home from the hospital. Some trivial clash of ideas had caused his mother to go home in a huff, leaving Clare in tears. He laughed them both out of the disagreement. But that was almost eight years ago. How long was he supposed to go on humouring them? Didn't they realise that young Danny was already starting to notice?

Without finishing his crossword, Jack refolded the paper and went upstairs to see if his son was asleep. He smiled fondly as he bent to kiss the sweet, innocent brow and he gently removed the pen which was still clutched in his hand. The letter Danny had written was lying on the floor. Jack picked it up and suddenly he was filled with consternation. He read most of what was written in a single glance.

My granny gives me drie bred and tea with no milk and she burns my toes and gives me cold shours and her dog colld Bessie . . .

Jack gave a shudder. The writing had stopped there, no doubt Danny had fallen asleep before he could finish — but his father was in no doubt that he had been about to add *bites me . . .*

He took the letter downstairs, wondering what Clare's reaction would be.

She glanced at it without removing her hands from the washing-up water.

"That boy needs some spelling lessons," she said, and laughed.

"Is that all you can say?" Jack demanded angrily. "What if he had sent that to the paper? I suppose it would please you to see my mother humiliated in public?"

Clare dried her hands and answered with great weariness and hurt. "If that's what you want to think, what can I say?"

"Honestly, Clare!" Jack exclaimed. But before he could continue the phone rang and he went to answer it, while Clare surreptitiously dried away a tear at the corner of her eye.

He returned a moment later.

"That was my mother. Danny left his teddy at her house — she's going to call in with it on her way to a party she's going to."

"I'd have thought she'd be too tired for a party after an afternoon of Danny," Clare said as she walked through to the sitting-room.

Transformation

THE rain slanted drearily, sleetingly down.
And a grey misty curtain enveloped the town.
It seemed as I watched, every joy must depart,
And I gazed with the tears of the world in my heart.

Then suddenly, radiantly, over the town
The sunshine appeared and dispelled every frown.
Every tear was forgotten as heaven's pure gold,
Made a picture of beauty each eye to behold.

— *Georgina Hall.*

"But what shall I do with this?" Jack asked worriedly, still holding Danny's letter. "What if she sees this?"

"Put it away in your pocket then," Clare replied indifferently. "If you want to deprive her of a good laugh."

"Do you think she would laugh?" Jack asked, frowning.

Instead of answering, Clare went to Danny's schoolbag.

"Have you looked at your son's workbook recently?"

She flicked through the jotter until she found the page she was looking for and displayed it silently.

At the top of the page was neatly printed *My Mother.* And underneath a sentence was scrawled. *Mie moter pushes me hard in the park . . .*

"He says that he didn't know how to spell swings," Clare commented wryly. "But it sounds pretty awful, doesn't it?"

Jack nodded.

"I wonder what his teacher thought —" then his jaw dropped as he read on. "How could he say that about me?" he said in injured tones.

My Father never gets up erly and he goes fishing witout me.

"Remember?" Clare smiled. "You didn't take him a couple of Sundays ago."

"But that was because he had a sore throat, and I was committed to going with Craig and Gregor."

"Where's the famous sense of humour now?" Clare asked, turning away.

Then as the doorbell rang she went to answer it, thinking sadly that Jack would never understand about being a parent.

W HAT are you looking so guilty about?" Julia asked her son as she entered the sitting-room.

Smiling, Clare turned to her husband.

"Jack, you may as well let your mother read it." And to Julia, she added, "I made Danny drink milk at suppertime, and Jack put jam on his bread — and I refused to rinse Danny with a cold shower."

To Jack's astonishment, Julia burst out laughing when she read what her grandson had written about her. Together, she and Clare laughed until the tears ran down their faces. Then Julia took out her compact and looked in the mirror.

"Now my mascara has run," she said, giggling. "It's just as well that little rascal isn't here to notice — he'd be writing in his school book — my granny had two black eyes. Isn't he priceless?"

"Maybe you wouldn't say that if his letter was printed in the paper," Jack answered rather stiffly. And he went on to tell her about the competition.

"Aren't you going to allow him to send it in?" Julia asked with a twinkle in her eyes, and then, sensing the strained atmosphere, she looked down.

Clare spoke rather awkwardly. "Jack didn't think you would be amused."

Julia gazed at Jack in genuine amazement.

"Didn't you?"

Then the two woman exchanged a look which he couldn't interpret

GREAT BRITON

ANDREW CARNEGIE

The millionaire industrialist and philanthropist Andrew Carnegie was born in Dunfermline, Fife, in 1835. He emigrated to America in 1848, where he eventually established the U.S. Steel Corporation. Carnegie gained a fortune from the sale of his business interests and with his millions he generously funded such institutions as libraries and universities in America and Scotland.

and Jack immediately felt confused and shut out from communications.

"I must say — this sudden show of solidarity is surprising to say the least," he said a little bitterly. And he turned his back on them both and stood gazing into the fire.

Julia rose swiftly to her feet and went to stand beside him.

"Jack, dear, we can't help it — I warned Clare before Danny was born that she'd have to put me in my place every so often. I told her that I had the world's worst time with my mother-in-law, when you and your sister were little."

"My gran?" Jack looked incredulous.

"Yes, dear." Julia sighed. "She kept criticising my modern methods and she spoiled you both at every opportunity."

She paused and softly touched his arm. "Truly, Jack, I don't mean to be nasty to Clare . . . it's just that we all love Danny, and we all have a part to play in his life — mine is to be the indulgent granny. But with a lively youngster like Danny there has to be a dragon too and I'm afraid that side of things falls to Clare."

Then she gave his arm a shake. "That's what's so funny about Danny's letter to the paper — he makes me sound like the biggest dragon of all time." She gave a chuckle. "I must go, I daren't start laughing again."

CLARE went to see her out and when she came back, she smiled at Jack and said, "We were just wondering what Danny's teacher would think if he wrote in his book about his granny going out on a date."

Then as she saw that Jack wasn't listening she frowned sadly.

He was sitting in the armchair, lost in gloomy thoughts. And she went to him and sat impulsively on his lap and put her arms around his neck and kissed him.

Jack wasn't unwilling to be kissed. He responded ardently.

"I don't think I'll ever understand women," Jack confessed. He paused and traced a line around her mouth with his finger. "All I know is that you're one in a million."

"No, no." Clare laughed. "That's your mother — a granny in a million — the competition, remember?"

He groaned and reached for the piece of paper which now lay on the coffee table.

"Does he really prefer dry bread?" he asked as he read it again.

"It's his latest food fad," Clare answered gaily.

"And I gave him jam." Jack sighed.

"Shame," she said with mock sympathy. But after a moment, she asked in a low voice, "Jack, do you really believe I'm jealous of your mother?"

"Not any more," he replied, "I didn't say it to hurt you, darling, but it did seem like that to me." He looked once more at his son's letter before he continued, "Maybe this wouldn't stand a chance in any competition, but it has taught me a lot — bad spelling and all."

Clare's eyes smiled lovingly into his, and then his lips found hers. □

UNABLE to sleep, yearning for and yet dreading the moment when she would leave home to catch the bus for the airport, Mandy was sitting at the window of the small room in the town where she had been born twenty-two years before.

She was overwhelmed now by a feeling of anti-climax, for her three weeks' holiday at her home on Deeside, even her long walks in the mountains, had only succeeded in convincing her that she didn't belong here any more.

In London, the solution to everything had seemed simple and obvious. But it had turned out to be no solution after all.

You can't go back in your tracks, Mandy thought. At least she had learned that much.

It seemed like hours since the thin grey light of dawn had broken through the mist of clouds. Now the sun had risen, transforming the sky into a rainbow of light and bathing the village in its glorious, golden glow.

Mandy watched the stranger — the man called Jock — strolling leisurely down the High Street, and tried to stifle the uneasiness caused by her parents' comments.

"We had a very odd young man to stay a couple of weeks ago," her mother had just told her. "He saw the bed-and-breakfast sign outside . . . he's coming again the night before you go back and travelling on the same plane."

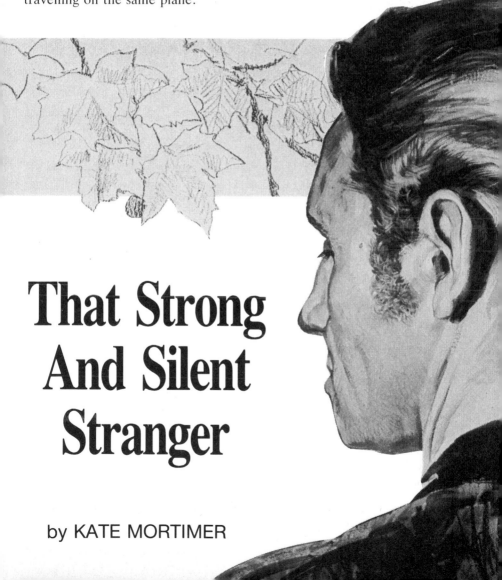

That Strong And Silent Stranger

by KATE MORTIMER

"So what?" said Mandy, who wasn't interested in young men, odd or otherwise.

"Well, he turned out to be rather interesting and pleasant. He was going on a walking tour."

"Hmm!" Mandy's father had interrupted. "If you ask me, there *is* something odd about that man. Your first impression was right. You just be careful, my lass."

"Nonsense," her mother said. "He just seemed odd at first. But it was only that he was reserved."

"Reserved my foot," Dad said tersely. "That man called Jock is plain secretive. I know he has something to hide."

Well, Mandy thought with a smile, the man certainly was different, and her father's instinct about folk was usually right. But what did it matter?

Since she, too, had something to hide from her parents, she hadn't intended to get into a discussion about the matter.

Luckily, her astute father hadn't apparently cottoned on to his elder daughter's unhappy state of mind. And Mandy didn't want to give herself away now. Some day she'd tell them.

HI!" The shout from the door made her jump and turn round. "You're awake. I'm so glad."

"Bless you, Anne, I was dying for a cuppa, but didn't want to go downstairs in case I woke you all up." Mandy smiled.

Her sister put the tray on the table and sat down beside her.

"Your last day," she said, looking at the elegant, blue travelling suit on the hanger. "It's been so lovely having you, 'cos you're still our Mandy underneath your smart London girl exterior. I'm almost grateful to that bug!"

"Yes, it did me a good turn, that flu, didn't it," Mandy said smoothly. The mythical "bug" had at least spared their feelings and accounted so conveniently for everything — her pallor, irritability, loss of weight . . . as well as suppressing her eagle-eyed father's instinct!

Anne poured out the tea and handed her a cup.

"You look great," she said. "You haven't got any spots," the younger girl added with a wry smile.

"When I was sixteen I had them — many more than you do! Anyway,

GREAT BRITON

EMMELINE PANKHURST

The English suffragette, Emmeline Pankhurst, was born in Manchester in 1858. Through such militant actions as arson, brick throwing and chaining themselves to railings, Emmeline and her followers succeeded in obtaining the vote for British women.

that Jim Reilly of yours doesn't seem to notice your spots."

"Nor should he," Anne grinned impishly, "since he's got so many of his own! He's so nice. I've had to promise him that I'll stay working in the village draper's and not go beetling off to a big London store like you!"

"Wise girl. You'd never meet anyone half as nice as Jim in London."

"I know." Anne smiled dreamily. "He is super. By the way, Mandy, you've never once mentioned that nice young man you told me about in your letters. He sounded like the answer to a maiden's prayer!"

"Oh well." Mandy put the empty cup down and turned to look out of the window. "He was quite nice in a way. But ships pass in the night, as they say, and we went our separate ways.

Anne's question had come just when she thought she'd escaped it. She'd hoped that no particular importance had been attached to Martin's name cropping up more and more often in her letters and then, just as quickly, disappearing.

"Do you mean he's left London?"

Mandy felt the heavy, grey shadow of misery and disillusion engulfing her again. But she kept her voice as steady and light hearted as she could, to keep her own spirits up.

"Yes, he's gone away . . ."

"And you — you don't give a hoot, you flirt!"

"I know. I'm dreadful! But in London, people do come and go and the world wags on its way, regardless."

Rose-Bay Willow Herb

IN the quiet lanes let none disturb
    Tall spikes of Rose-Bay Willow
    Herb,
Unless it be a butterfly,
Or bumble-bee in passing by,
Discovering their roseate charm
By roadside ditches, bank and farm.

In the tussocked grass their regal spires
Outshine wild roses' blushing fires,
Soft blending in with creamy white
Of meadowsweet of lesser height,
To grace the sultry summer day
In an unassuming gentle way.

In the quiet lanes let none disturb
Tall spikes of Rose-Bay Willow Herb,
That soon would droop if gathered from
The open air they thrive upon,
That look so splendid where they
    grow,
With wine-pink florets all aglow.
                    Violet Hall.

"And all you really care about is your career." Anne sounded just a little doubtful.

"That's right. I intend to be buyer in the gown department some day. But go and put some more water in the pot." Mandy changed her tone. "I want another cup of tea."

At the door Anne turned round.

"All the same, I don't believe you hardly noticed that smasher who came here last night and, lucky you, he's going on your flight."

"No I didn't, specially. And I don't expect to see him once we leave home. Besides, you know what Dad thinks?"

"Yes, but I reckon he's off beam this time. I reckon Jock's just different and anyway, he could have something on his mind."

It was just before she went down to breakfast that Mandy saw Jock returning from his walk — carrying a large bulging plastic bag. So, he'd been to fetch something, though as none of the shops were open yet, she couldn't imagine what it was.

Mandy pulled herself up with a jerk. What business was it of hers?

IN the airport bus, she sat with her mother, who was going to see her off, and Jock sat behind them, but he didn't speak until they were on their way out to the plane.

"This . . . staying in your parents' house last night, was a wonderful finish to my trip," he said.

"Thank you," Mandy said politely.

But her intention of dodging him in the plane was thwarted, and as

GREAT BRITON

AMY JOHNSON

Famed aviator, Amy Johnson, was born in Hull in 1903. Amy was the first woman to fly solo from England to Australia, and she was also noted for breaking other flying records in the Thirties. While a pilot in the Air Transport Auxiliary during the Second World War, Amy tragically drowned after baling out of her aircraft over the Thames estuary.

they zoomed skywards he was in the seat beside her, as if quite unaware of her indifference, even hostility.

"I'd been to see a friend in Spain," he said easily, and certainly without evidence of shyness. "His parents have one of those houses they rent out to tourists. All very exotic. But give me Scotland any day — even the weather. I hate all that heat in the southern countries!"

He went on chatting, still not seeming to notice her lack of response.

"Your parents are so wonderful — your mother's a sturdy tree that can bend to the wind without breaking. And your father . . ." He stopped.

That Strong And Silent Stranger

Mandy, all of a sudden, was startled by this man's insight. "And what did you make of my father?" she asked in spite of herself.

"I . . . well let's say I wouldn't like to cross him!" The young man laughed. "I had a feeling he didn't quite approve of me."

How could he have understood so much, so quickly? Mandy glanced down at the brown hands resting on his khaki, corduroy trousers.

FOR the first time she wondered about him. Who was he? What did he do? Those long, slender fingers had certainly never done any manual work.

What kind of man would be so clever, so chatty, yet still reserved, unrevealing about himself?

An actor travelling incognito? A writer gathering material for a book? A detective on a trail . . .? She pulled herself together.

"Your impressions are uncanny. But I assure you my father would only think you were . . . well, different from the usual bed-and-breakfast people they entertain."

"I have been feeling a bit guilty about arriving in the middle of your farewell party, and then not joining in when I was asked."

"Not to worry," Mandy assured him. "Nobody gave it a thought. After all you've been on a long walking trip, anyway." She paused, not wanting to offend him, but not wanting to talk to him any more, either.

"Actually," she said quietly, "I'm feeling a bit whacked after the party. Please don't think me frightfully rude, but I could do with a sleep."

"You couldn't be rude if you tried," he assured her. "You go ahead and have your forty winks!"

Now, Mandy thought, she needn't say another word. She could feign sleep for the rest of the way.

She turned her head away and gazed down at the fluffy white clouds drifting together, separating, undulating beneath the plane like graceful, lace-clad ballerinas, revealing in their movements brief glimpses of the country below.

It was so beautiful, soothing and inspiring. Mandy began to feel calmer. But as soon as she closed her eyes, she saw another sky . . . and the sea . . . and the white cliffs at Brighton the day Martin drove her down there for the first time.

SHE'D met him in the staff restaurant at the store. He worked in the Accounts Department and he'd told her even that first day she should set her sights high, plan to have her own boutique. He had even told her how easy it is to borrow money to start such business schemes.

But of course she'd just laughed at the idea of *her*, Mandy Jamieson, borrowing huge sums of money for anything.

He'd seemed to understand, because he didn't talk about it again. The drives to the sea, to the country, were a joy to her. Martin was so different from anyone she'd ever known, so easy in his manner, so sophisticated.

Sometimes, when they'd gone to an exotic restaurant for a meal, she'd wished her family could see Martin's way with head waiters.

And then, so suddenly there was no Martin, and even now she didn't know exactly why. She only knew that he disappeared not only out of her life, but from his job at the store. There were many rumours, but the only certain thing was that for some reason Martin had been sacked because there was "something wrong with his bookkeeping."

Mandy shivered, remembering the chat she'd had with the head of her department.

"He was a . . . sort of . . . friend of yours, wasn't he?" she'd said to her.

"Well yes, sort of," she'd replied automatically.

"I'm glad that's all. He was a charmer, but . . ." The voice had tailed away, and no more was said.

But Mandy shivered again, recalling the shock of it all, the uncertainty, and the silence. She knew it was silly of her, but she'd felt contaminated. And so she'd decided to go home for a holiday, perhaps for good. Maybe she would return to the little draper's shop where she'd first gone to work after leaving school.

NOW it seemed incredible she'd ever thought that possible. At home she was Mandy Jamieson, the girl who'd made good and gone to a posh job in London, and she now realised she was the odd one out in the family. She could never go back, only forward to whatever the future may hold.

"Stop pretending to be asleep." The voice in her ear was very quiet. "You're shivering like a leaf in a gale! I want to show you what I was fetching this morning. Oh yes, I saw you at your window."

He opened the plastic bag and she looked inside.

"Heather!" She gasped.

"Yes, very special for a very special person." He took a wallet from his pocket and a snapshot from one of its compartments. "See, it is for this very special young lady in my life."

Mandy gazed, enchanted, at the picture of a golden-haired little girl with rosy cheeks and dancing, blue eyes. She looked about three years old and was posing, with wondrous grace, in a mass of frilled yellow cotton beside a flower bed of red roses.

Mandy felt strangely uplifted by the joyousness in the child's innocent expression.

"She's a darling," she breathed. There is something . . . something special about her . . . a sort of . . ."

"Radiance?"

"Yes, that's just it."

She turned to the man, now at ease with him.

"She's a star," he said, "and she sheds that radiance on everyone. She's one of the reasons I've persisted and made myself a nuisance to you, when you were so obviously wishing me anywhere else in the world than beside you in this plane."

"I'm sorry . . . I . . ." Mandy felt herself blushing.

"Don't worry, I fully understand. Blushing suits you, by the way!"

"Is she . . . is she your daughter?" Mandy stammered.

"No, I'm not married. She is my brother's daughter — and she's the patient of a colleague."

"You're a doctor?" Mandy gasped. Yes, that would explain everything, the reticence, the strength, the shrewdness.

"I'm going to be a surgeon," he told her.

Mandy instinctively looked at his hands — strong and yet so delicate.

"But this child . . . you sounded as if . . . but there isn't anything wrong with her. Is there? She looks so full of life and glowing health."

"She was, and she will be again," he told her. "But she had an accident . . ."

"Will she be all right?" Mandy interrupted him.

"Yes, eventually. My colleague operated on her and it's going to be a success. Only it'll take a long time."

"And the heather is for her?"

"Yes, she loves it, though she hasn't a clue what it's called! Her father has been to see her, but he goes away again tomorrow. He's on an oil tanker . . ."

"Oh dear . . . she'll miss him. And her mother?"

"Yes. It's her mother I'm most worried about — she's had to take the brunt of it all. Now she'll be needing a listening ear."

"A what?" Mandy asked, baffled.

"I mean that she's a bit sick of blatherers. She needs someone who's been through the mill too. Someone who will understand, and transcend the maudlin pity she's so fed up with!

"It doesn't matter what, or why, Mandy. But I believe you are — or have been — going through one of life's bad patches." He smiled down at her. "Not just a dose of flu. Don't worry, we medics sense these things."

"I can't talk about it," she said swiftly.

"You don't have to until . . . if you ever wish to. But I wanted to break down the barrier and reach the real you, for your sake and my niece's mother."

"But what in the world can I do?"

"You can meet her, talk to her," he said simply. "You see, I know you'll say all the right things and none of the wrong ones . . . because you'll understand. Would you do that? Will you allow me to take you to meet her?"

MANDY looked down at the green earth below them. For the first time in three months she could see a pointer, a step in the right direction.

She looked up at Jock, and smiled at him — her brightest smile for many a long day.

"Yes, of course I'll meet her. I'd love to."

"Atta girl, and bless you." Jock squeezed her arm. "I thought you were a fine brave girl who'd know one can build on disaster — if one tries!" □

AT RAINBOW'S

by ELSPETH RAE

KAREN McKENNA looked at the plate of congealing bacon and eggs which she had put down at her brother's place ten minutes before, and bit her lip in annoyance. "Andrew!" she shouted impatiently.

When there was no response she stormed through into the boy's bedroom. He was still in bed, eyes closed as though asleep. Karen knew better though — she had seen the tell-tale flicker of his eyelids. She grabbed his shoulder and shook him roughly. "It takes me all my time to make ends meet without wasting good food," she began irately.

Andrew sat up straight, scowling. His red hair rumpled and his eyes bleary with sleep, he looked much younger than his seventeen years. "What is there to get up for anyway?" he demanded. "I'm not expected anywhere, am I?"

"You could go down to the Jobcentre," Karen started.

"What for? I've been going there every day for a year now, and it hasn't done much good. Has it?"

"But you must keep trying, Andy," Karen said.

"It's all right for you, you're one of the lucky ones. You don't know what it feels like to wake up every morning with an empty day ahead of you and no money to buy anything. I don't feel like trying any more, thank you very much. So go away and let me sleep."

Since their gran had died three years ago Andrew had been Karen's responsibility. At that time, even though she had been only twenty-two, she had not felt it a great load. Living in Blackthorn was not like living in a town. She was surrounded by folk who had known the McKennas all their days, and there were always plenty of people to whom she could turn for help. Only in this past year, with Andrew out of school and unable to find a job, she had begun to feel the strain of her combined rôle of mother, father, and wage earner.

There were times like this morning when she felt little bubbles of panic begin to rise inside her. What was going to become of Andrew if he didn't find a job soon? The trouble was he hadn't passed a single "O"-level exam. Not that he was stupid — he just wasn't academic. He had all sorts of practical skills. His friends always brought their motor-bikes to Andrew first, rather than spend money at the local garage, and nine times out of ten he was able to repair them.

He could decorate a room like a professional, and he could turn out a decent-looking bedside table or a stool if you supplied him with the wood. Unfortunately, none of these qualities seemed to be wanted in the job market at the moment, and Andrew was becoming more and

END

more despondent and bitter. There were three or four lads in Blackthorn who were constantly in trouble with the police. Karen's dread was that Andrew would be sucked into this set.

KAREN had been eight years old, Andrew a baby, when their parents' car had met a fatally treacherous patch of black ice one winter night seventeen years ago. Had she not possessed photographs of her father and mother, she could not have remembered how they looked. Yet this morning she missed them with all the sharpness of a recent loss. Mother would have taken Andrew in hand, Dad would have known how to guide him.

Then as she turned the corner to walk the few remaining yards to the bus stop, Karen gave a muted groan. Mrs Clarke, her least favourite neighbour, was standing there, hand on her shopping trolley, eyes glinting behind her spectacles as she caught her sight of Karen.

Mrs Clarke had come to live in Blackthorn two years ago, and in Karen's opinion was the biggest bore in the village, since her idea of a conversation was to try to impress you by telling you the extortionate prices of everything she bought, as well as boasting about her posh relatives. She was also one of those elderly people who can find nothing but bad in the younger generation.

"Well! Did you hear those motorbikes last night? I'll swear they were up and down that lane for a good two hours! I thought I'd go mad. They have no consideration at all today, these young ones."

"I didn't hear them," Karen said shortly.

"Well I expect that young brother of yours was playing his records so loudly, you couldn't hear anything else. I don't know how they don't all go deaf! And how can they afford to buy records anyway, living on the dole? My goodness! What a cushy life they have, compared to my young days. No wonder they don't want to work!"

Karen gave a strangled gasp. She felt the blood rush to her cheeks. Luckily the bus arrived at that moment or she might have said something she would later have regretted. She hurried upstairs, knowing that Mrs Clarke, hampered by her shopping trolley, would not follow. She sat and fumed inwardly during the half-hour's journey into town. Honestly! The woman was impossible! And there she was with all her money, probably never having wanted for anything in her life!

KAREN did not know that Mr Rae, the manager of the bank where she worked, regarded her as his most reliable teller. But she enjoyed her work and took a pride in doing it as well as she could. She was vexed that morning when she twice made a mistake in counting out notes for customers. After the second incident, Mr Rae watched the pretty blonde girl for a while, his eyes thoughtful. Young Karen had something on her mind this morning. That was obvious.

He felt so sorry for the lass sometimes, especially when he thought of his own daughters and the carefree lives they had led at Karen's age. Karen had been burdened with her invalid grandmother, then with a home and a young brother at a time when other girls had nothing on their minds but boyfriends, clothes and everything to do with romance.

An idea suddenly came to Mr Rae. He and his wife had organised a theatre party for that evening to see a performance of "Bitter Sweet." He was sure they would be able to buy an extra ticket. He waited until Karen was having her coffee break, then went through to join her. He explained about the theatre party.

"Would you like to join us?" he asked. "You look as though you could do with an evening out."

"Oh, that's very kind of you!" said Karen gratefully. "But this is the evening of the village Coal Dole, and I've promised to help. I'll be sitting in the village hall from seven until nine taking down the names of the pensioners who qualify for three free bags of coal."

"Ah, well! Perhaps another time," said Mr Rae with a smile. "But try to give yourself a treat once in a while, Karen. You know what they say about 'All work and no play.' "

"Still, better than 'All play and no work,' as my brother would tell you," Karen remarked with a sigh, as she went back through to her desk.

A T ten minutes to seven that evening Karen was sitting behind a table at the back of Blackthorn Village Hall with a stack of application forms before her. Mrs Girvan, the minister's wife, was seated at another table a few feet away.

"I should imagine we'll have a lot of customers this evening," she called over to Karen. "The price coal is nowadays the old folk need all the help they can get."

Karen nodded and smiled a shade absent-mindedly. For the last few minutes she had been watching the young man who was standing in the doorway talking to Mr Girvan. Steven Forbes was Blackthorn's most popular GP, and the more Karen heard of his kindness the more she was drawn towards him. He was so attractive, too, with those warm, dark eyes of his!

"But he doesn't even know I exist," Karen had confided morosely to her friend, Ginny, who worked in the bank with her.

"What does he do in his spare time?" Ginny had asked.

"Plays tennis," Karen told her.

"Well! Go on, then!" Ginny had urged. "Join the tennis club!"

It was too late for that, though, Karen thought wryly as she saw Dr Forbes leave. At the age when people joined clubs, she had been fully occupied, trying to combine caring for Gran and Andrew with a job. She had never even attempted to take part in the social life of the village's younger set. She couldn't suddenly break into their circle now, at twenty-five! Yet recently she had begun to feel that life was passing her by, that she ought to take up some new interests. Once Andrew was settled in a job, she would have time to look around her. But when would that be?

As the clock struck seven, Mr Girvan opened the door and the village's elderly folk began filing in. As one familiar face after another passed before Karen, the heap of completed application forms grew higher. Then, looking up to greet her next customer, Karen's mouth dropped open. She couldn't believe her eyes. For there before her, a bland smile on her face, stood Mrs Clarke!

If Karen had not still been smarting from Mrs Clarke's innuendo about Andrew that morning, she might not have reacted as she did. As it was, her face flamed and she was unable to conceal her indignation.

"Mrs Clarke," she began, tight lipped, "you obviously don't realise that this coal is meant for people who have to struggle to buy it. It's not intended as a free gift for every over-sixty in the village, no matter how well off."

Mrs Clarke's rouged cheeks turned a little redder. "Dear me," she said loudly. "I certainly wouldn't want to take what I wasn't entitled to. I was obviously misinformed by the person who told me to come along."

"And who was that? Mr Greedy?" Karen muttered under her breath as Mrs Clarke turned away.

GREAT BRITON

T. E. LAWRENCE

Lawrence of Arabia was born Thomas Edward Lawrence in the Welsh town of Tremadoc in 1888. A scholar and a soldier, he fought in the Arab revolt against the Turks in the First World War. The book, "The Seven Pillars Of Wisdom," which he wrote when he was a Fellow of All Souls', Oxford, recounts his experiences.

She saw Mrs Girvan glancing over, but she had no time to discuss the matter with her either then or later. As Karen walked home, something else happened which pushed the thought of Mrs Clarke's effrontery right to the back of her mind. When she was about a hundred yards from the village's only pub, she saw a group of the local "undesirables" emerging from it. In the middle of them, plainly visible, was Andrew's red head.

A LL next day, the worry about Andrew niggled at Karen like a toothache. She had gone to bed without airing her feelings the night before, because of the fear that a quarrel might alienate her brother from her. I've got to hold on to him, she kept telling herself. I must! For Mum's, Dad's and Gran's sake, as well as his own.

By the time she got home that night she was still undecided as to what to do about the problem. She had a splitting headache, not helped by Andrew's being out, a note on the table telling her only that he would be back at eight. She began to worry about where he might be.

So tensed up was she, that when the doorbell rang at six-thirty, she started so violently that she spilled hot tea down the front of her dress. Mopping it with the tea-towel, she hurried to the door to find Dr Forbes on the step.

The doctor's normally smiling face looked troubled, almost angry, as he greeted Karen briefly. "May I come in for a moment?" he asked.

Despite her preoccupations with Andrew, Karen's heart still raced a little as she led the young man into the sitting-room, then turned to look at him enquiringly.

"The truth is, Miss McKenna," he began abruptly, "I'm extremely annoyed with you. You undid months of good work last night with certain comments you made."

"I did?" Karen stared at him in bewilderment.

"Indeed," he went on. "Last winter, on more than one occasion, I found Mrs Clarke living in rooms so cold that she was in danger of succumbing to hypothermia."

"Well, she could well afford heating . . ." Karen began. But the doctor interrupted her.

"Mrs Clarke can afford very little," he said briskly. "She has only her pension, and every week out of that she sends something to an invalid sister."

"That's nonsense!" Karen exclaimed indignantly. "She never stops telling people how much she's been spending."

"She's proud," Dr Forbes said, "stupidly proud. She invents all sorts of fantasies to hide the real state of affairs. That's why no-one has been asked into her house since she came here. It's taken me months to persuade her to swallow her pride and apply for the benefits she's entitled to. And as I've already said, you've probably wrecked all I've accomplished with your few ill-chosen words last night.

"I was furious when Mrs Girvan told me about it. Even if Mrs Clarke had been well off, it wasn't your place to turn down her application."

SUDDENLY Karen felt as humiliated as a schoolgirl being scolded by a teacher. "Well, if Mrs Clarke hadn't been so objectionable yesterday morning, it would never have happened!" she burst out. "Going on about my brother not wanting to work, when he's been hunting for a job for a year now, becoming more depressed and difficult every day. I'm sure I don't know what's going to happen to him . . ." Before she could stop herself, Karen was weeping uncontrollably.

"Oh dear! Goodness me! You've been bottling things up and no mistake!" Steven Forbes' voice had changed. He put a hand on Karen's shoulder and guided her gently towards the settee. "Sit there," he said. "Have your cry while I make a pot of tea. Then you can tell me all about it."

Ten minutes later Karen, red eyed, and still giving an occasional hiccuping sob, unburdened herself to Dr Forbes. When she had finished, he drew a notebook from his pocket.

"Right," he began in a businesslike manner. "Now tell me anything that might be in Andrew's favour. What can he do well, for instance? And what are his good points?"

"Why do you want to know?" Karen asked the young man, when she had answered as fully as she could.

"I have a wide variety of patients," he told her as he rose to leave. "I'll ask around and see if any of the small tradesmen or businessmen might be interested in employing a lively, enthusiastic young lad."

Karen's face lit up. "Oh, that is good of you!" she exclaimed. "Thank you very much!"

"I'm not promising anything, mind you," Steven said cautiously.

"But at least it gives us some hope." Karen smiled. "We haven't had any of that for a long time." Then her smile faded. "I am sorry about Mrs Clarke," she went on. "Perhaps if you explained I was irritable because I was worried about Andrew . . . ?"

"May I?" Steven asked.

Karen nodded. "She might feel better if she knows she's not the only one with problems."

"It might help her to be more understanding, too," Dr Forbes said quietly as he left.

THREE days later, on Friday morning, Karen was shaken awake by an excited Andrew. He was holding a letter.

"It's from a Mr Cairns in Crossburn," he explained. "Dr Forbes told him about me, and he wants me to go over and see him. He restores antique furniture and he'd been thinking of taking an assistant on for some time, he says. He doesn't care about the 'O'-levels. Oh, Karen! It'd be just up my street. I could cycle there and save the bus fares. It's only five miles."

"Go this morning," Karen urged him. "Show him how keen you are. Put on your best trousers and a clean shirt. And don't be shy! Speak up for yourself."

"Oh, I do hope he's not turned down!" Karen sighed to Mr Rae at her coffee break that morning. "I won't know what to do with him if he is."

"I'm sure it'll be all right," Mr Rae said comfortingly. "Andrew's a nice lad with a pleasant manner and a good appearance. This is just the sort of opening that would suit him."

Nevertheless, Karen was unable to relax until she jumped down from the bus that afternoon to find a grinning Andrew standing waiting for her at the stop.

"Hurry up, Sis!" he said. "I've cooked a celebration tea. I start work on Monday!"

It was amazing, Karen thought as she hurried along beside the tall, young lad. There was a visible transformation in Andrew already. Yesterday he had slouched, now he was striding along, straight backed, chin up, as though he owned Blackthorn.

He had made his speciality, spaghetti bolognese, and had bought cakes from the village shop.

"Delicious!" was Karen's verdict.

"Now I'm going to wash the dishes," he announced. "So you can put your feet up."

But Karen stood hesitantly in the kitchen doorway. "You haven't seen Dr Forbes yet?" she asked.

"I rang the surgery at lunchtime, but he was out," Andrew told her.

"Then I think I'll walk down there now," Karen told him. "I'll catch him at the end of his evening surgery. I don't want him to think we're ungrateful."

K AREN and Andrew were registered with Dr Howie, Steven Forbes' senior partner, but since they both enjoyed good health, Karen had not been in the surgery in the three years since her gran had died.

"Andrew got the job with Mr Cairns," she announced with a smile, as the young doctor rose to greet her. "I can't tell you how grateful we are!"

"Good!" Steven exclaimed with a sigh of relief. "I'm sure he'll be happy there. Jim Cairns is a grand fellow."

"What about Mrs Clarke?" Karen asked a shade anxiously. "Have you had a talk with her?"

"Yes, I have." He smiled. "She'll be all right next winter, I think. She realises she's been acting foolishly . . ." He paused suddenly. "Why not come out for dinner with me tomorrow evening and I'll tell you all about it?" he suggested.

Karen was so taken aback she couldn't find her tongue.

"It's all right," Steven assured her. "You are registered as Dr Howie's patient. I checked with him." Then realising that he had given himself away, he blushed. "OK, I admit it," he went on. "I've been planning to ask you out ever since that evening I called on you. It was your smile that did it. The one you gave me when I said I'd ask around about a job for your brother. A doctor needs a smile like that in his life. Will you bring it to dinner with you?" he added gently.

"Yes," Karen replied, "with pleasure."

"I'll pick you up at eight," he said, his dark eyes shining down into hers as he accompanied her to the door.

The smile refused to leave Karen's happy, flushed face as she made her way home. Mrs Clarke, who was standing at her gate, got the benefit of it.

"What a lovely evening!" the elderly lady heard herself say. And to her surprise she realised that she meant it. Suddenly she decided she was going to ask some friends to tea on Sunday afternoon, and she hurried off indoors to look out some of her old recipes.

"It is a lovely evening!" Karen echoed, as she went lightly on her way along the road. □

GREAT BRITON

BRONTE SISTERS

The beautiful Yorkshire town of Haworth is famed for being the birthplace of the three Bronte sisters, Charlotte (1816), Emily Jane (1818), and Anne (1820). The daughters of a clergyman, they led isolated lives, writing mainly about their own immediate area of Yorkshire. The parsonage in which they lived is now a museum dedicated to those three famous Haworth women.

She's Leaving Home

by ELLEN JANE MACLEOD

BELINDA stood staring at her father, her pale face registering both disbelief and horror. "But, Daddy, you can't mean it," she said, pleading as only a nine-year-old girl can.

David Lockhart sighed as he held his daughter close. "My dear wee Lindy, do try to understand," he whispered into her soft brown hair, using the pet name he always used whenever there was a crisis on, like a skinned knee or having to go to the dentist.

Belinda closed her eyes and leaned against him. This was like a nightmare, she thought, fighting back the tears. Her own wonderful daddy was going to get married again. Someone was coming to live with them in this lovely house in Glasgow, someone who was going to take her mother's place.

At the thought of her wonderful mother, who died two years ago,

with her soft voice and gentle laugh, who tucked her in bed each night with a kiss, Belinda's control snapped. Sobbing as if her heart would break, she broke away from her father's arms and flew upstairs, her sobs echoing down to the white-faced man below.

David sighed. He knew it was going to be a hard job to convince his little girl that he was not putting anyone in her mother's place. No-one could ever do that. Jean and he had been happily married for ten years. No-one could take those memories away. And it was not as if Isobel Leslie was a stranger. The Lockharts had known her ever since Belinda was born when she moved in next door.

He walked slowly towards the hallway. How could he explain how lonely he had been since her mother had died? He was afraid Belinda had been very lonely, too. He knew how she missed her mother. The many nights he had gone into her room when her sobs had penetrated the wall between them.

He hesitated at the foot of the stairs. The sobs had stopped, making the silence even more unbearable. Yet he waited — perhaps it would be better to leave her alone. She might get used to the idea if she had time to think about it. He had tried not to spring his news too suddenly on her, but there was no way he could hide the fact that he intended to marry Isobel.

But Belinda was not thinking about anything at that moment. She had cried herself out on top of her bed and now lay staring dry eyed at the ceiling where the shadows of evening were making strange patterns. She loved her father so much. A quick flash on her memory screen showed her father and herself on one of their usual Sunday walks through Kelvingrove Park. The stops for tea and buns at their favourite little café, and back home to Mrs Mason, their housekeeper, and one of her delicious dinners.

THE memories nearly brought the tears again. She sniffed loudly to stop them. It had been lovely until last year when Miss Leslie joined them. It was not that she did not like Miss Leslie, she did. She was a lot of fun. She had really made her last birthday party. And all those lovely bedtime stories she could tell. But not to live with her and Daddy for ever.

She slipped off the bed and wandered over to the window. She glanced furtively next door where she had a good view of Miss Leslie's back door. She caught a glimpse of the slim figure at the kitchen window going from the sink to the stove. She wondered if she was making some of those lovely gingerbread men.

She remembered the first time Miss Leslie had brought some of them over for her when she was getting over the mumps. They had tasted simply wonderful. The mere thought of them and the lovely smell of ginger suddenly reminded her she was hungry.

She could hear Mrs Mason moving around the kitchen downstairs, the clattering of pans mingling with the hiss of water, as she filled the kettle. She was about to turn from the window when the slam of the kitchen door made her glance out again. Her mouth quivered and tears filled her eyes as she watched her father walk briskly across the back lawn and up the two steps to Miss Leslie's kitchen door. Loneliness swept over her in one huge wave. Her daddy had gone to her and had not even come upstairs to see if she wanted him. She felt rejected.

"Oh, Mummy! How could he?" she moaned softly, turning away blindly and heading for her wardrobe. Opening it, she pushed aside her own collection of clothes until her hand felt the soft, velvety touch of her mother's dressing gown. It was her most precious possession and the only thing she had of her beloved mother. "What can I do?" she choked, burying her face into the lovely soft folds of the material.

As the sobs slowly died down, she wiped her eyes with the back of her hand. "Daddy doesn't want me."

She closed the wardrobe and went downstairs. Mrs Mason turned from the sink. She started to speak but one look at the woebegone little face and she turned away, shaking her head. So Mr Lockhart had told Belinda his plans . . .

A Precious Moment

WHEN winter weaves its web of lace
  On every pane of glass,
And coats with fondant icing
  Each tiny blade of grass.

When crackling ice begins to form
  Upon the village ponds,
And fir trees bow in tribute
  Their snow-encrusted fronds.

When clearly through the crystal air
  You hear the wild geese call,
And robins watch in silence
  As snowflakes gently fall.

Remember that this lovely scene
  Was never meant to last,
So hold it in your memory,
  For winter soon will pass.
      — B. Heaton.

"Go wash your hands, dear. Dinner is almost ready."

Silently, Belinda turned and went back upstairs to the bathroom. Mrs Mason's sympathetic eyes followed the child. "Poor Mr Lockhart," she murmured. "He's been dreading telling the bairn."

ISOBEL LESLIE'S worried eyes looked at the tall man whom she had promised to marry and wished with all her heart she could comfort him or, at least, give him some good advice. But Belinda was his child.

"She'll get used to the idea, David," she whispered, but somehow her words sounded hollow in her own ears.

"If you could have heard those sobs," David said brokenly. "Even when her mother died, she took it less hard."

"But she is two years older, don't forget." David looked puzzled. "She thinks she is losing you, too. You're all she has."

"Oh, Isobel, what would I do without you, my love?" he whispered, drawing her close to him. The kiss he gave her comforted Isobel more than anything he could have said.

But to the watching eyes of the little girl peering out of her window, it was the end of everything. With a strangled sob, Belinda flew over to the wardrobe again, flinging the doors open. Snatching her mother's dressing gown, she stuffed it into her schoolbag. Slipping on her red wool coat, she felt in the pocket for her purse. Daddy had given her some money to spend on a treat so she would use it now.

Quietly creeping down the stairs again, she tiptoed towards the front door. Carefully opening it, she slipped outside, quietly closing it behind her. The evening shadows were now rain clouds and already Belinda felt the light drops on her face, but her heart was too full of grief even to be frightened by the darkness which turned Fairmont Avenue into an unfamiliar place. With one glance back at the Leslie house, she disappeared down the street and out of sight.

"I better get back now," David whispered. "Mrs Mason will have dinner ready."

"I'll see you later, dear?"

"I have some paperwork to do, and then I'll be back." He smiled, kissing her warmly. "I'll see Belinda into bed first."

"Don't worry too much," Isobel murmured. "Belinda is a very intelligent little girl. She'll think it all out. You, as a schoolteacher, can't miss her mental ability."

"I know. See you later."

Mrs Mason glanced up at David as he came through the kitchen door. His face and hair were wet. "It would rain tonight when I have to go out." She smiled, trying to ignore the pale, set face of her employer.

"Belinda already down for dinner?"

"I just sent her up to wash her hands. She should be down in a minute."

TEN minutes later, standing by the dining table, David frowned at Belinda's empty place, then at Mrs Mason, who was bringing in some cutlery.

She doesn't usually take so long to wash her hands."

"Shall I give her a shout, Mr Lockhart?"

"No, thanks. I'll run up and find her." He dashed up the stairs with an uneasy feeling. "Belinda! Dinner's ready," he called through the closed bedroom door. "Do you hear me?" His voice had gone sharp with anxiety as only silence answered his call. Flinging the door open, he strode in, anger on his face. "Belinda, stop sulking and come down at once to . . ." His voice faded at the sight of the empty room. "Belinda!"

"Mr Lockhart! What's wrong?" Mrs Mason's worried voice preceded her into the room. "Is she not here?"

But David had already disappeared into the hall towards the bathroom. He knew before he got there that it would be empty. The other rooms were the same.

"How long ago did you send her upstairs to wash her hands?"

David's steely voice frightened the housekeeper. "A few minutes before you came in."

"Right! She couldn't have gone far." At the sight of Mrs Mason's white face, he tried to smile. "She's probably gone over to Vera's house." He patted her shoulders. "Go tell Miss Leslie. She might know what else to do."

Mrs Mason hurried away to get her raincoat but David was already rushing out the front door to see if he could see her before he started phoning her friends.

Isobel's face whitened when Mrs Mason told her the news. "She's run away?" But she knew the answer before the housekeeper nodded. "She could have gone next door to Judy's or across the street to Vera's or even Peggy's farther along. I'll phone them now."

But Belinda was not at any of her friends' and when David returned home half an hour later, there was still no Belinda.

ISOBEL and David stared at each other, their shocked faces registering the fear they both felt. They had been so sure Belinda would be home again when they returned. She had never done anything like this before.

"I thought she liked you," David said. "She is always talking about your lovely home, your wonderful cooking and the nice clothes you wear."

"That's different from me marrying her daddy," Isobel said dully. "You'll have to call the police, David."

"She hasn't been gone an hour yet," he reasoned. "We must give her time. You've phoned everyone?"

"Everyone, dear. Oh, David what have we done to her?"

"Nothing," he said sharply. "We'll both talk to her together."

Isobel nodded. "We'll give her another hour . . . no more!" Isobel said firmly. "Glasgow is such a big place at night for a child, even though it is early."

To Belinda, Glasgow seemed even bigger. At first, the novelty of seeing the lit shop windows along the empty, wet Sauchiehall Street fascinated her. Even the heartbreak of losing her daddy to someone else was dwarfed by the excitement of being all alone. She had never been out herself at night before.

The rain streaming down her cheeks and dampening her wool coat made her suddenly aware that she could not keep going like this. What should she do? It all seemed so easy just to leave home and want to go somewhere else. On she trudged, unaware of the curious stares from people driving past. Carefully crossing at the lights as she had been taught, she found herself walking into a darker street. Frightened, she turned back and headed for Hope Street. But the traffic was quicker there and she turned again, fleeing back to Sauchiehall Street, the street she knew well.

Tears were mingling with the rain on her face now and she dabbed them away furiously with the back of her hand. She could not go home now, Daddy would be angry with her.

Suddenly staring ahead at the empty street again, she saw two policemen turn a corner and head towards her. Terrified, she quickly slid into a dark doorway and waited. The heavy footsteps approached her hiding place and she could hear their voices. One of them suddenly laughed and it sounded just like Daddy's laugh when she had done something funny to please him. For a moment the happy, familiar sound recalled David's strong face.

The tears began in earnest now. She wanted to go home but Daddy did not want or need her any more. He had Miss Leslie. She slipped out of the doorway and stamped on, her schoolbag bumping against her side. She did not even notice the pouring rain now soaking her feet.

THERE was something about tonight that reminded Belinda of something. Then a quick flash of Miss Leslie's smiling face brought it all back. The little girl came to a standstill as she recalled another wet night just like tonight when she had come home from the Brownies soaking wet. Miss Leslie had run out of her house into their kitchen and made her change her clothes right away.

She also remembered the lovely hot drink afterwards. The sound of Isobel's kind, worried voice came to her mind and suddenly she knew she just had to go home again whether they wanted her or not. She wanted them.

Clutching her schoolbag higher, she began to run as fast as she could back to Fairmont Avenue, her breath becoming sobs at the thought that perhaps her daddy would not want her back.

She had just reached the corner of Fairmont Avenue and had stopped to catch her breath, when suddenly two strong arms caught her up into the air and held her close. Belinda snuggled into her father's neck, clinging as tightly as she could for fear he would suddenly disappear.

"Oh, Lindy! How could you? We've all been so worried. You know we both love you," he whispered into her ear.

"I love you both, too, Daddy," she said wearily, snuggling even closer as he strode back home with her. She peered over his shoulder and saw Miss Leslie looking anxiously down the street, the rain beating into her face. She waved and smiled when she caught sight of Belinda. Belinda waved back and sighed contentedly.

She was safe now. Nothing mattered any more. Her daddy and Miss Leslie loved and wanted her, and she really did like Miss Leslie an awful lot . . . . □

A beautiful sunny view looking towards Aonach Dubh and the snow-capped top of Stob-Coire nan Lochan (3657 ft.) in Glencoe. The rugged character of this Argyllshire countryside is breathtaking, and visitors to this celebrated area cannot fail to be impressed by the sheer magnificence of the glen with its grand mountains and fast-flowing rivers. Although Glencoe is often thought to be at its most moody and forbidding when it is misty, sunshine brings out the colour and vital beauty of this wild landscape.

D. Hardley.

GLENCOE

B^Y some kind of miracle, Selina Bailey avoided a collision with little Jeremy's tricycle which had stopped unexpectedly outside her front gate. On an ordinary day, she would have undoubtedly ended up with torn tights and bruises, because Selina was that kind of person. Accidents didn't wait to happen to her, they rushed to meet her.

But this was no run-of-the mill day, it was her twenty-first birthday and she was going to do her utmost to leave it unscarred.

"You'd better be more careful, my lad."

She paused in her rush to work to chide the toddler gently. Taking hold of the trike's handle-bars, she guided its little passenger towards his own garden. She'd already noticed the open side gate, usually securely fastened. Did Jeremy's mother, Shirley, know? She was usually so careful.

by JEAN MURRIE

ON THIS SPECIAL DAY

Jeremy twisted round and, gazing up at his favourite neighbour, remembered past kindnesses.

"Take me brambling again," he instructed. "Now."

"I'm off to work just now, Jeremy," she explained patiently.

Anxiously she glanced up the road. Luck was still with her — the bus was late.

"After, then." Persistence was Jeremy's hallmark.

"I'm sorry, love. Ray is taking me out."

Jeremy's eyes lit up. Ray had found the very best brambles on their expedition last weekend.

"Me come too," he added confidently.

"Another time," she replied hurriedly, stooping to give him a quick kiss.

Her bus had just rounded the corner. She mustn't miss it and get off to a bad start even before the day had properly begun. This day just *had* to be right all the way through.

October

OCTOBER'S time means winter's near,
As winds grow cold and breezes sere,
Yet golden leaves still flow down
From trees in country and in town.

Time of haze and time of sun,
Time to hurry and be done
With summer things that have passed;
Wintertime is here at last.

Winter, when the snow falls white
And dreamlike, in the long dark night;
When ponds become glistening delight
To skate upon in graceful flight.

O. Little.

"Tomorrow, then." His brown eyes were appealing, and the bus was drawing dangerously close.

"All right," she agreed. "Tomorrow."

What on earth made her make such a rash undertaking, she wondered, as she settled into her seat. What would Ray say? Their first full day as a properly engaged couple and she'd committed herself to take a toddler brambling!

There she was again, her heart ruling her head. If this day was to run as smoothly as she had planned, then she would have to react more wisely to situations. However, she ought to find time to advise Shirley of the unfastened gate. She would ring her when she got to work.

But when she reached the department store where she was employed, the place was already busy with weekend shoppers, and Mrs Smart, the check-out supervisor, urged Selina to take her place behind the till as quickly as possible.

SELINA worked steadily, allowing no untoward circumstances to ruffle her composure. She'd lived the last few days very prudently, and was about to reap the reward.

Celebrating a twenty-first birthday in style was not so usual these days, but this was her second chance to celebrate her coming-of-age. Her eighteenth birthday had been a fiasco. Her parents had planned a party for her, but the day before, she had foolishly agreed to sample Aunt Mollie's notorious walnut pickle, and had consequently spent her birthday in bed.

Today was more than just a birthday celebration, though. Ray would place on her finger the beautiful diamond ring they had chosen together, the symbol of their love, and the outward sign of the pledges they had already made to each other.

She remembered to phone Shirley at coffee-break time, but the number was engaged. Relaxing with her cuppa, she indulged in a little day-dreaming, recalling the lovely afternoon she, Ray and Jeremy had spent last week, wandering through the old brickworks, searching for the most laden bushes.

Jeremy had strode gamely through the neglected vegetation, clutching his seaside bucket, determined to fill it to the brim with luscious fruit, whilst his elders meandered more slowly, dividing their attention between each other and the task in hand.

Even now, she could feel the fat berries so ripe that just a touch sent them rolling over her hand into the waiting basket. Around them rose the pungent scent of crushed fruit as they stretched ever deeper into the cavernous bushes covering the garden of the watchman's derelict cottage.

She experienced again the scratchy dryness of the long grass as they all flopped down, hot and tired, on the bank of the canal to eat their lunch.

GREAT BRITON

ALEXANDER GRAHAM BELL

Scientist Alexander Graham Bell was born in 1847 in Edinburgh. After emigrating to America, he pioneered the first successful telephone transmission. This came about from his research in speech mechanics carried out while training teachers for the deaf. The Bell Telephone Company was set up by Bell himself, who was later responsible for producing the first successful phonograph record.

Only little things, but etched sharply on her memory because Ray shared them with her.

It was on such an outing that she had met him two years previously.

"Good grief, has he come to pick berries or to model for a country casual collection?" Selina had muttered when she'd first set eyes on Ray as he'd strolled out of Aunt Mollie's house where he had temporary lodgings until his own flat was ready. He was a newcomer to the area, recently employed in the same company where Mollie worked.

Mollie threw her niece a sharp glance.

"Just you keep that unruly tongue of yours still," she warned as Selina slipped into the rear of her aunt's car.

Selina wasn't an unkind girl at all, but she did have a rather off-beat brand of humour and often spoke without thinking.

"Remember, he comes from a very nice city family. I think he looks rather smart, though his clothes are a little too good for the activity on which he's about to embark!"

D URING the drive out to the country, conversation had been rather stilted. The two young people didn't appear to have a great deal in common. Ray talked about the London theatre and books that had been reviewed in the Sunday papers. Selina mentioned her two cats, a favourite recipe for blackberry wine, and the barn dance to be held in aid of the local conservationists.

As they uncoiled from the car, she was aware of his eyes upon her, and was momentarily discomfitted about her appearance, the jeans and jumper that had seen better days. She tilted her head defiantly. She was dressed for the job, whereas Ray's smooth cords and unsnagged sweater had apparently never been near a thorn bush.

Mollie's pursed lips indicated she'd been thinking along the same lines.

"Bill always leaves his gardening clothes in the boot of the car," she said. "If you put them on, Ray, you'll protect your good clothes."

Mollie fetched her husband's gear and after a moment's hesitation Ray slipped out of sight to reappear a minute later in clothing that swamped his slender frame.

Selina was speechless. Mollie's guest looked absolutely ridiculous. Unable to keep her face straight she turned away, but not before Ray had noticed. His carefully constructed composure slipped, he looked down at himself and laughed. Soon all three were convulsed with mirth. The ice had been broken.

Then their tongues worked as quickly as their hands, and wit sparked off each other. Selina and Ray discovered they enjoyed the same TV comedies and cartoon strips.

By the time they put their loaded tubs into the car, Ray knew he'd made a firm friend in his new town, and Selina had met someone at last who could see beyond the disorganised exterior to the person of sense and ability beneath.

T HAT was two years ago, but Ray dominated her dreaming and planning. It seemed he had always been part of her life.

At five-to-one, Mrs Smart approached her.

"Could you please delay your lunch break for half an hour?" she pleaded. "Mrs Pierce, your relief, has missed her bus."

Selina scanned the long line of harassed mums and restless children. She knew that if she insisted on taking her lunch break at the proper time, the till would have to be closed. Even as she agreed to stay, she inwardly riled at the hiccup in the smooth, easy running of her day.

When she eventually arrived breathless at the salon where she'd planned to have her hair done in preparation for the evening's celebration, Tracey, her usual stylist, was already working on her next client.

"If you can wait a while, I can squeeze you in before my two o'clock," she suggested.

Selina reflected on the chaos back at the store.

"Or Vicki can do it for you," Tracey added helpfully, referring to the newly-qualified assistant.

Selina acquiesced, and Vicki tackled her hair enthusiastically.

"It's your twenty-first, isn't it?" Tracey called across. "Have an extra-special rinse on me."

When Vicki had finished, Selina looked perturbed at the image staring back at her from the mirror. The young assistant had cut her hair much shorter than she was accustomed to, and the coppery rinse glowed.

"It's fine, thanks," Selina reassured her. Vicki beamed.

It was the sort of style a lot of young people liked, but it wasn't what she wanted. Why did things always seem to turn out badly for her? Ray always managed to land on his feet, no matter what happened.

MORE GREAT READING!

If you've enjoyed the stories you've read here, then the heart-warming, delightful stories — both complete and continued — which appear every week in "The People's Friend" are certain to please, too. The magazine also contains imaginative cookery recipes, helpful knitting and dressmaking patterns, colourful scenic pages and many popular features for all ages.

For information about subscription rates, ask your local newsagent or write to: Subscribers' Dept., People's Friend, Bank Street, Dundee DD1 9HU.

She kept her strange new head down for the rest of the afternoon, and it passed without incident, Mrs Smart even letting her away a few minutes early.

"I do like your new hairstyle," her mother commented at once, genuinely pleased, when Selina arrived home. After she'd been told the tale of the delayed lunch hour and its consequences, she was glad that for once, misfortune had worked in her daughter's favour.

She heartily approved of this forthcoming engagement. Selina had flourished under Ray's care and devotion, he'd given her confidence, calmed her down.

He, too, had changed. The stiff, city gent, whom she'd first regarded with some misgivings, had mellowed into a warm, kindly man. Their love for each other was a joy to behold.

As she watched her daughter opening cards and gifts that had arrived for her during the day, she decided not to mar her happiness by telling her of Shirley's visit. No doubt the small crisis would be resolved by now.

A S Selina dressed with care in the sophisticated grey suit she thought just right for the occasion, the doorbell rang. What a pleasant surprise for Ray to find her ready for once!

But it wasn't Ray's voice she heard raised in agitation. By the time she reached the bottom of the stairs, the visitor had gone.

"That was Shirley," her mother told her, distressed. "I didn't want to worry you but Jeremy has been missing for nearly an hour. He's wandered off before, but this is the longest he's been away. Shirley's just realised his red bucket is missing and thinks he may have gone brambling. Do you have any idea where he may have gone?"

Selina knew with absolute certainty where he'd be. Kicking off her high heels, she thrust her feet into walking shoes and fled down the road, across the playing fields towards the old brickworks. The canal was quite a bit further on but in an hour, a toddler could cover a lot of ground.

She choked back sobs of rage against herself. She'd forgotten to warn Shirley about the garden gate, but just now she couldn't afford to indulge in self-pity.

The enticing, laden bushes at the watchman's old cottage drew near. Holding her breath in hope, she veered towards them and caught a glimpse of a blonde head in the midst of the thickest bush. Jeremy's whimperings turned into wails when he saw her.

"Selina, I'm stuck. All scratched." He struggled to reach her but was firmly held by long thorny tentacles.

As Selina waded through the knee-high grass to reach him she noticed with horror a wasp hovering near his face. Jeremy saw it too, and screamed in panic.

With supreme effort, she lunged forward sufficiently to be able to grip him firmly and haul him clear. They both staggered backwards on to the ground and it was then she realised what a sorry state she was in. The elegant suit was woefully snagged and her hands were scratched and bleeding.

"Oh, Jeremy, what have you done?" she murmured. But the toddler was too happy to be free of his thorny prison to pay much heed to what his rescuer was saying.

Ray, handsome in smart sports jacket and slacks, was anxiously

▶ *p172*

Church spires and Georgian buildings give the Fair City of Perth an air of antiquity , yet today it is a bustling town with a modern centre. The church of St Leonard's in Marshall Place is a very attractive building with a distinctive spire looking on to the tree-lined parkland of the South Inch, carpeted in this restful springtime scene by a profusion of purple crocuses.

R. W. Weir.

ST LEONARD'S IN THE FIELDS CHURCH, PERTH

waiting for her when she returned home. She was almost in tears at the realisation that her little escapade might ruin their evening.

But Ray's concern was all for her injured hands. He bathed them gently as a grateful Shirley repeated what Jeremy had told her of his ordeal.

"This suit is not fit to be seen in," Selina grieved. "Why didn't I stop to think before I dashed into those bushes?"

"And Jeremy might have been badly stung," he reminded her. "Go and change into your yellow dress." As she hesitated he added, "I like it, and it will be cooler on a warm evening like this."

She quickly made repairs to her appearance with a lightening heart. Ray's understanding was the best balm of all.

O N the way to the bus stop, she chatted cheerfully of the trials of the day, now fallen into their proper perspective. Ray listened sympathetically and like her mother, agreed that the set-back at the hairdresser's was not a disaster at all. She looked beautiful tonight.

However, when he proferred their fares to the bus driver, he said tersely, "Two to the park, please."

Selina looked at him in consternation as they took their seats. "Why, Ray?"

"The restaurant table I booked will be taken now." He avoided her eyes and added, "Anyway, I think the Park Restaurant will be more suitable." He offered no further explanation and lapsed into glum silence.

Selina could scarcely believe the sudden change of mood as well as of plan. She glanced at the cotton frock and hastily-donned summer jacket. She was hardly dressed for an expensive eating place. And despite his earlier assurances, Ray must mind about that after all.

He hurried her through the park, mysterious and romantic in the gathering dusk, but wasted on Ray in his present frame of mind. Selina tagged on as best as she could in her ridiculously high-heeled shoes.

On they rushed towards the café on the far side of the boating lake on which she and Ray had spent many a happy hour. But there was no trace of that joy in the glowering face beside her now.

As they seated themselves at a corner table, the waitress looked meaningfully at the clock on the wall.

"I'll just have a hamburger," Selina said miserably, not even glancing at the menu.

"Make that two, please," Ray added without interest, as the waitress hovered. "And a couple of colas."

Selina bit into the half-cold food delivered to their table with amazing speed but she could scarcely swallow it. She couldn't believe how badly everything had turned out.

Less than an hour ago, she'd been ready to enjoy the best evening of her life and now she could only stare at her grim-faced companion through the gloom of the half-lit café. What a disaster it all was!

Tears welled into her eyes and filled her nose and throat. She sniffed furiously and groped into her pocket for the hankie that wasn't there.

Ray pushed his neatly-folded one into her hand. The little gesture overwhelmed her and a loud sob escaped. The waitress stared at her curiously. Ray would be mortified.

"I'm sorry," she managed to say. "I'm hopeless."

"Yes, you are hopeless," he chided. "Why do you always blame yourself when things go wrong? It's my fault we're here, not yours."

She glanced up at him, to see he was serious.

"I changed out of my suit before I called for you," he explained, "because it was a warm evening . . . and I forgot my wallet. I only had enough money to get us to the park."

"You could have asked me to pay," Selina said.

"It was to be your perfect evening. I knew how much you'd looked forward to it and how much you'd gone through already today! Anyway, you'll have to pay for the food."

HE joked, but Selina detected that all was still not well.

"You could have chosen worse," she reassured brightly. "The park has always been one of our favourite spots, hasn't it? We can become engaged anywhere."

"Without a ring?" Ray queried.

At Selina's look of surprise, he confessed.

"I had the ring in my other jacket pocket, too. And yes, I forgot it. I couldn't bear to tell you. If you hadn't been hanging on so tightly I would have run into the lake, not past it! You're not a bit upset, are you?" he asked, as mirth transformed her face.

"Let's say it evens the score a bit. Oh, I've done some awfully silly things in my life, but this must take the biscuit!" She chortled.

"We're still learning new things about each other, aren't we? Do you have any more surprises in store, Ray?"

"Not at the moment, but we'll change," he said earnestly, "both of us, and grow more like each other. It's something to look forward to."

Selina caught his hand and held it tenderly between hers.

"You don't need a ring to get engaged," she said softly.

"No, of course not, but I want everyone to know that you're willing to have me, stuffy old shirt that I am!"

Quickly, Selina twisted the ring-pull from the soft drink can and passed it to him. Gravely, he slipped it on to her finger.

"Will you marry me?"

"Yes, oh yes." She breathed with exaggerated rapture.

Under the unbelieving eye of the waitress, they kissed.

"We'll do it properly tomorrow," he promised later as they wandered, arms entwined, through the soft September evening. "Posh clothes, elegant restaurant, diamond ring and all."

"Great!" Selina thought of her promise to a certain golden-haired toddler. But how about a spot of brambling first?" □

Printed and published in Great Britain by D. C. Thomson & Co., Ltd., Dundee, Glasgow, London and Manchester.
© D. C. Thomson & Co., Ltd., 1986.
ISBN 0-85116-378-5

J. Campbell Kerr.